Ages 5-6

Kindergarten
Made Easy

Canadian Edition

MATH · SCIENCE ·
SPELLING · LANGUAGE ARTS

Authors
Anne Flounders (Language Arts)
Linda Ruggieri (Math, Spelling)
Hugh Westrup (Science)

Canadian educational consultant
Marilyn Wilson

Penguin Random House

Managing Editor Barbara Campbell
Editors Nancy Ellwood, Camilla Gersh, Jolyon Goddard,
Margaret Parrish, Allison Singer
Educational Consultants Kara Pranikoff, Alison Tribley,
Marilyn Wilson
Senior Editors Fran Baines, Cécile Landau
Senior Designer Marisa Renzullo
Art Director Martin Wilson
Pre-production Editor Francesca Wardell
Pre-production Manager Sunil Sharma
Senior DTP Designer Pushpak Tyagi

First Canadian Edition, 2015
DK Canada
320 Front Street West, 11th floor
Toronto, Ontario M5V 3B6

Copyright © 2015 Dorling Kindersley Limited
A Penguin Random House Company
10 9 8 7 6 5 4 3 2 1
001–271942–Aug/2015

DK books are available at special discounts when purchased in bulk for
corporate sales, sales promotions, premiums, fund-raising, or educational
use. For details, please contact specialmarkets@dk.com.

Printed and bound in China by C&C Offset Printing Co.

All images © Dorling Kindersley Limited
For further information see: www.dkimages.com

A WORLD OF IDEAS:
SEE ALL THERE IS TO KNOW

www.dk.com

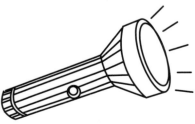

Contents

This chart lists all the topics in the book. Once you have completed each page, stick a star in the correct box below.

K Math

Note to parents

This section is intended to assist children studying math at the kindergarten level. The math covered will be similar to what children are taught before and during kindergarten programs.

Contents
By working through this section, your child will practise:
- reading, writing, counting, and adding to 10;
- finding more than, less than, and fewer than;
- recognizing differences and similarities;
- completing patterns and describing, comparing, and drawing shapes;
- measuring and comparing quantity, size, length, and width of objects;
- subtracting, or taking away one and more than one;
- sorting objects into sets, adding sets, and finding totals;
- using positional words, such as *top*, *bottom*, *above*, *below*, and others;
- drawing larger and heavier objects;
- telling and writing the time;
- recognizing money and counting coins.

How to help your child
Your child's reading ability may not be up to the level of some of the more advanced math words, so be prepared to assist. Working with your child also has great benefits in helping you understand how he or she is thinking and reasoning, so that areas of difficulty for your child can be more easily determined.

Often, similar problems and concepts will be worded in different ways such as "count one more" and "which has more?" This is intentional and meant to make children aware that the same basic concepts can be expressed in different ways.

When appropriate, use props to help your child visualize solutions—for example, have a collection of coins to use for the money problems, or find examples of objects to measure around your house.

Build children's confidence with words of praise. If they are getting answers wrong, then encourage them to try again another time.

Answers are found at the back of the book, along with further notes and tips for helping your child.

⭐ Count 1 to 5

GOAL

Practise counting from 1 to 5.

1 2 3 4 5

How many stars are there in each row?
Circle the correct number.

   2 3 4

   2 3 4

   1 2 3

★ ★ ★ ★ ★   3 4 5

Write the two missing numbers on each line.

1   2   4

    2   3   5

1   3   4   5

123456789123456789 12

Practise counting from 6 to 10.

How many apples are there in each row?
Circle the correct number.

 5   6   7

 6   7   8

 5   8   9

 6   8   10

Circle any ten flowers below.

Count up to 10

Practise counting up to 10.

5 6 7 8 9 10

How many objects are there in each box?
Write the correct number.

10

8

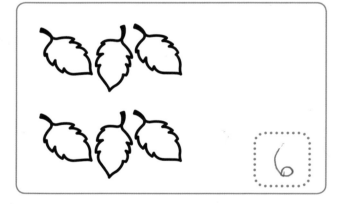

6

9

Write the missing numbers in the boxes.

2 1 2 3   4 5 6

2 7 8 9   0 1 2

2 3 4 5

4

GOAL

Practise counting up to 10.

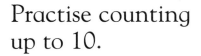

5 6 7 8 9 10

Look at the ten houses along the trail. Write the numbers that are missing in the circle next to each house.

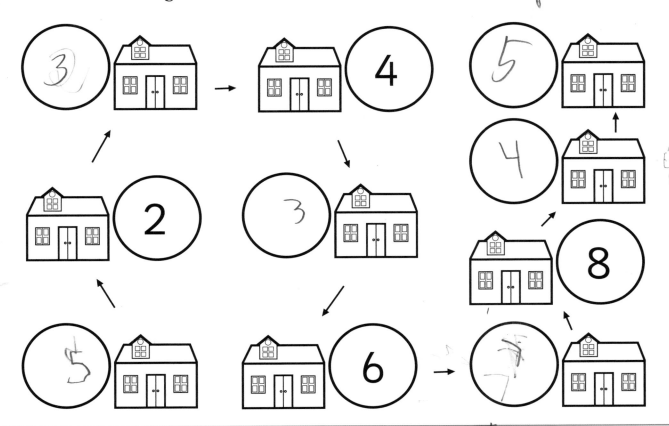

Count ten doors. Cross out the extra doors. Then write the number 10 in the box.

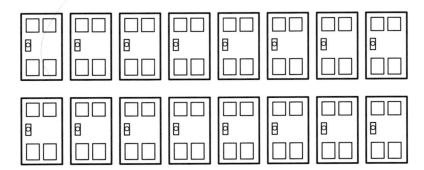

Add different numbers from 1 to 9 to make 10.

Count each group of toys. Write the correct number
of toys in the box.

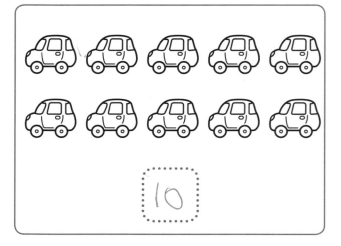

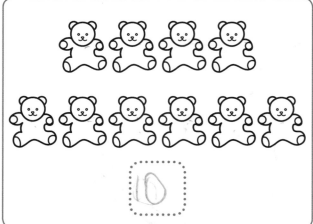

10

10

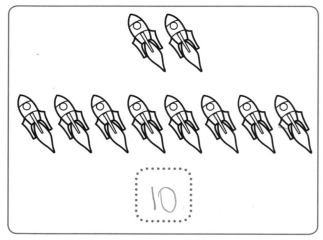

10

10

Copy the pattern of dots on the other side of the domino.

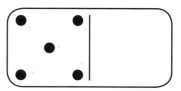

Now count all the dots on the domino,
and write the correct number.

5

5   5 5

5 5 5

Review how to make 10.

Write the numbers from 1 to 10 in the circles next to each car on the path below.

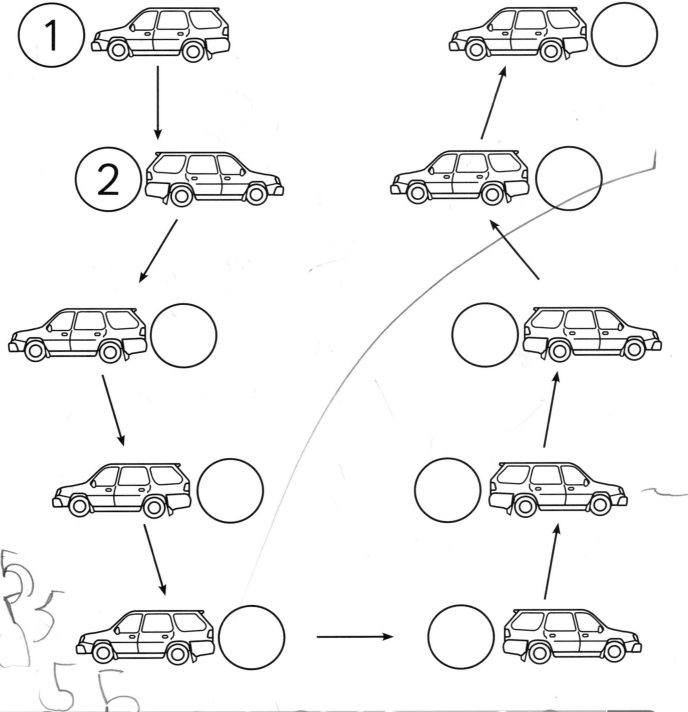

Learn about making sets of 10.

Count the objects in each box. Add the correct number to make 10.

How many boats did you add?

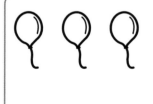 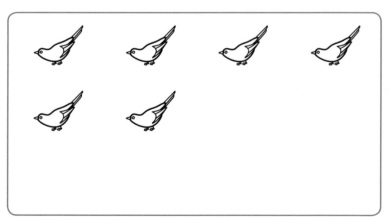

How many balloons did you add?

How many birds did you add?

GOAL

Review ways to make 10.

Draw the number of objects to make 10. The first one has been done for you

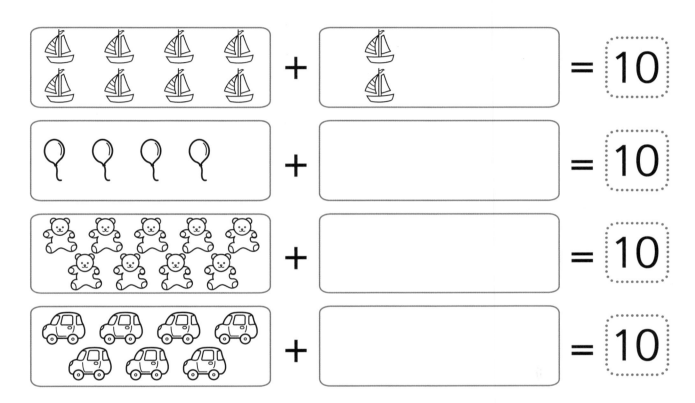

Follow the path to the castle and write the missing numbers on each stone.

Castle

GOAL

Learn that objects have shapes, and shapes have names.

Look at the objects. Circle the correct shape of the object in each row.

The cookie has the shape of a   square   circle

The door has the shape of a   rectangle   triangle

The pool has the shape of an   square   oval

The tree has the shape of a   circle   triangle

Circle the word to describe the shape of this ball.

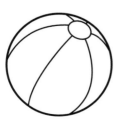

square   circle   triangle

Different shapes

Learn to identify different shapes.

Look at the shapes in each row. Circle the shape that is different.

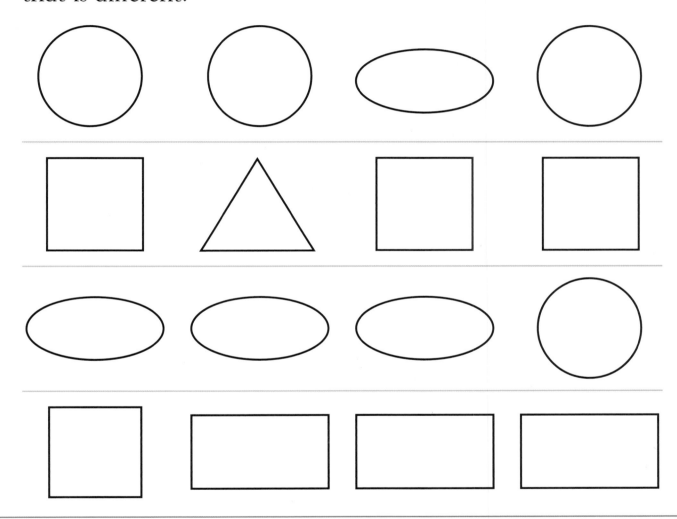

Draw five triangles below. Then draw a silly face on each one.

GOAL

Describe shapes by the number of sides and corners.

Circle the word that correctly completes each sentence.

A square has four corners and .... sides.

three   four

A circle is ....

round   straight

A rectangle has four corners and is ....

round   long

A triangle has three corners and .... sides.

two   three

Circle the triangle that is larger than the others.

 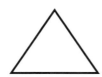 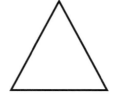 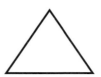

Shapes can vary in size. Learn to find the shapes that are larger.

Look at the shapes in each box. Colour in the largest shape.

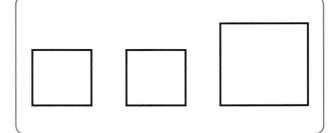

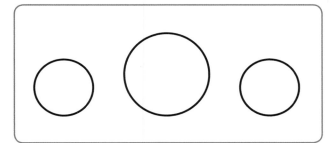

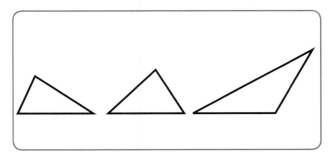

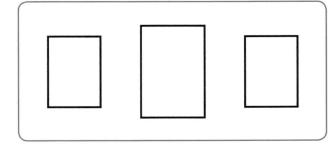

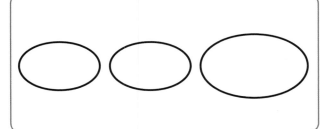

Circle the shape that has four sides.

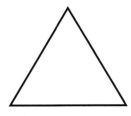 

GOAL

Learn to draw shapes.

Look at each shape and make it into an object.

Draw a circle
and make it
into the sun.

Draw a square
and make it
into a present.

Draw a triangle
and make it
into a hat.

Draw an oval
and make it
into a face.

123456789123456789 12

GOAL

Practise finding and counting shapes.

Colour the circles red. ◯ Colour the rectangles yellow. ▭

Colour the squares blue. ☐ Colour the triangles green. △

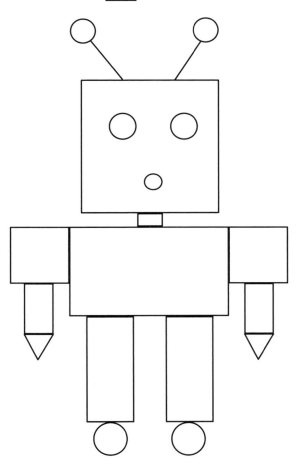

How many of each shape is there in the robot?
Write the correct numbers in the boxes below.

☐ squares   ☐ circles

☐ triangles   ☐ rectangles

⭐ Shape patterns

GOAL

Learn to draw shapes and continue patterns.
Patterns are repeated sets of objects.

Draw the shape to continue the pattern in each row.

....

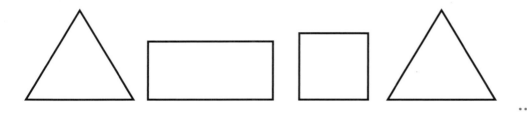

....

....

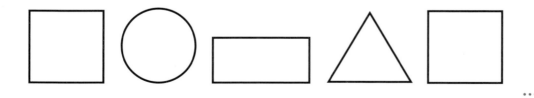

....

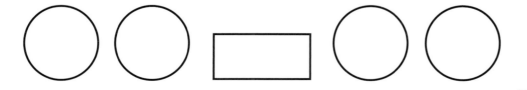

....

1234567891234567 8912

Practise continuing patterns.

Look at the cupcakes below. In each row, follow the pattern and decorate the tops of the undecorated cupcakes with the correct design.

Look at the pattern of the cookies below. Draw two more cookies to continue the pattern.

....

GOAL

Learn to identify objects that are the same.

Look at each row of animals. Circle the two animals that are the same.

Circle the two fish that have the same number on them.

Learn to compare characteristics, such as numbers and letters.

Put the balls into the correct boxes: Draw a line from each ball with a number on it to the number box. Draw a line from each ball with a letter on it to the letter box.

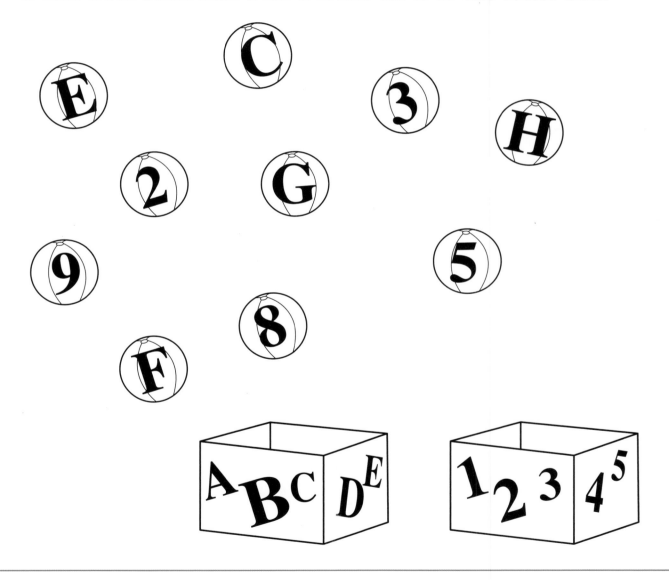

How many balls are there altogether?

Learn to find things that are not the same, or different.

Circle the leaf in each row that is different.

Circle the six flowers that are the same.

Learn to identify (spot) which is different.

Circle the animal in each row that is different.

Add spots to the frog on the right to make the two frogs look the same.

Count the objects to find out which set has more.

Write the letter **M** on the line under the box that has more objects.

 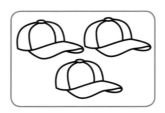 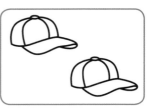

....

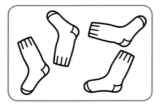 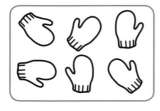 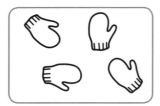 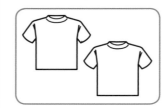 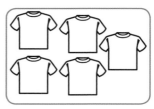

....

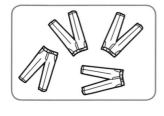 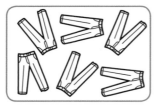 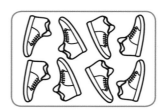 

....

How many sneakers are there below? To find out, count how many are in each pair, then add up the numbers.

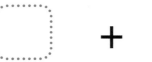 +  +

⬜ + ⬜ + ⬜ = ⬜

1 2 3 4 5 6 7 8 9 1 2 3 4 5 6 7 8 9 1 2

Learn to add one more.

Add one more to each group in the boxes. Then count the total items in the group and write the correct number.

Draw one more balloon, then count the balloons.
How many are there altogether?

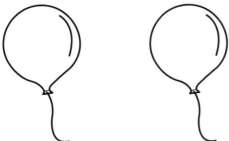

Draw more shapes to add to the group. The + sign means to add.

○ + ○○ = 3

Draw two more of the same shape in each box. Then add all the shapes and write the correct number.

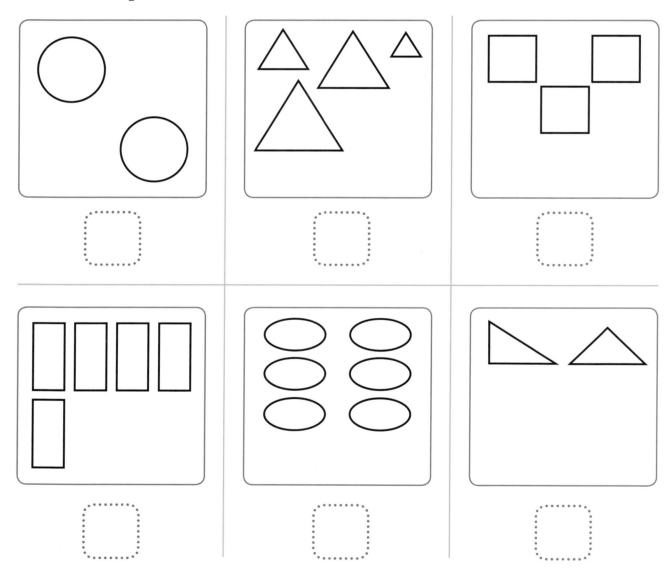

How many triangles are there on this page? Circle the answer.

7   9   10

Find the total, which is the answer you get when you add things together.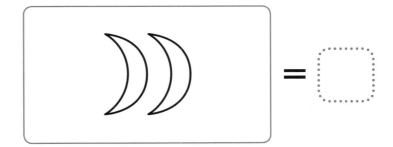

Draw a + sign between the boxes in each row. Then count all the items in both of the boxes and write the total number.

  =

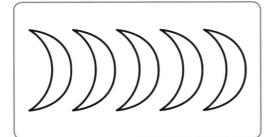  =

 =

In total, how many stars are there on this page? Circle the answer.

5   7   10

Find the group that has fewer objects.

Look at the baked goods below. For each treat, circle the group that has fewer than the other.

cakes

cupcakes

cookies

pies

Count all the cupcakes above. How many are there?

1234567891234567891 2

Take away one object so that a group has one fewer.  2

Look at the pictures in each row. Cross out one of the pictures. Then count the remaining pictures and write the correct number in the box.
Remember: Do not count the picture with the X on it.

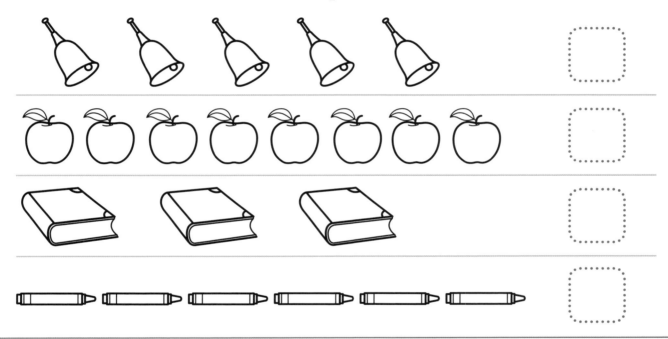

Count the cups below that are not crossed out.
Circle the correct number.

7   8   9

GOAL

Cross out to show taking away more than one. Count to find how many are left.

   `1`

Cross out two vegetables in each row. Then count how many are left. Write the correct number in the box.
Remember: Do not count the vegetables you crossed out.

    ⬚

      ⬚

        ⬚

Read the counting poem below. Write the words to complete the poem.

One potato, two potato, ... potato, four!

Five potato, ... potato, seven potato, more!

Practise subtracting, which means to take away. Then count how many are left.

3

Cross out three of the animals in each box to subtract them. Then count the animals left in the box.
Remember: Do not count the animals that have an X.

bear

How many bears are left?

rabbit

How many rabbits are left?

Read the poem below. Then write the word to finish the poem.

I saw four birds in a tree.
One flew away, and then there were ....

GOAL

Add together groups to make sets of ten.

Draw a line from the group in the first column to the group in the second column that makes a set of ten.

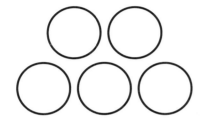
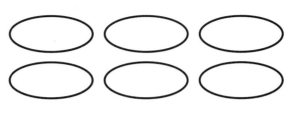

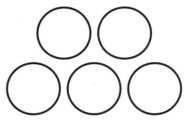

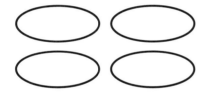
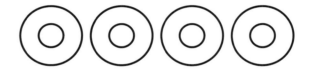

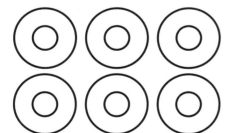

Circle a set of ten crayons below.

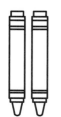 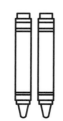 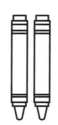   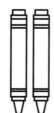 

Learn to sort items into groups that are the same.

Draw a line to match the number on each child's shirt to the numbers on the flags below.

Count all of the children on this page. How many are there?

GOAL

Learn to match sets and find pairs.

Look at these socks. Find and match the correct pairs.

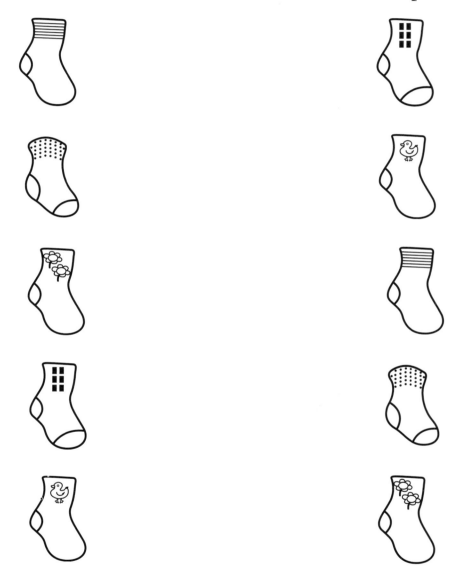

How many sets, or pairs, of socks are there above?
Circle the correct number.

5   6   8

Count to find the number of things in each set.

Count the farm animals in each box below. Then write the correct number of animals next to each box.

Count the chickens and the chicks. How many are there altogether? Circle the correct number.

7   14   16

Compare the sizes of two objects to find the biggest.

Circle the biggest animal in each row below.

Draw a bigger turtle in the box.

Draw bigger or smaller

Learn to draw objects that are bigger or smaller.

GOAL

Look at each picture, and follow the directions.

Draw a bigger sun.

Draw a bigger flower.

Draw a smaller star.

GOAL

Compare the lengths of two objects to find which is shorter and which is longer.

Look at each row carefully. Follow the directions.

Circle the longer snake.

Circle the shorter penguin.

Circle the horse with the shorter tail.

Circle the animal with the longer legs.

Circle the girl whose hair is longer.

123456789123456789 12

Learn to draw objects that are longer or shorter.

Look at each picture. Follow the directions for each.

Longer

Draw a fish that is longer.

Shorter

Draw a bird with a shorter beak.

Look at the snake. How many dots long is this snake?
Count the dots, and circle the correct number.

12   18   20

Compare weight

GOAL

Compare the weights of objects to find the heaviest.

Which weighs more? Circle the heavier object in each box.

Meg's cat weighs 4 kilograms.
Her dog weighs 7 kilograms.
Which weighs more?

....

1 2 3 4 5 6 7 8 9 1 2 3 4 5 6 7 8 9 1 2

Learn to draw things that are heavier or lighter.

Look at the mouse below. In the empty box, draw
an animal that is heavier than a mouse.

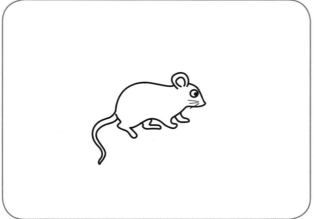

Look at the elephant below. In the empty box, draw
an animal that is lighter than an elephant.

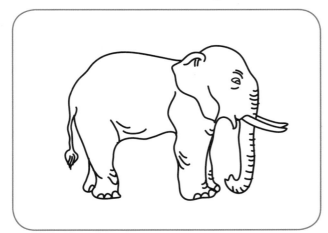

Look at the three animals.
Circle the animal that
is the heaviest.

Learn position words, which tell us where an object is placed.

Look at the picture below. Circle the words to answer each question.

Where is the squirrel?	next to the tree	up in the tree
Where is the bird's nest?	below the tree branch	on the tree branch
Where are the children?	up in the tree	in front of the tree

Look at the insects below. Which one is in the middle? Circle the insect in the middle.

Review position words:

inside	outside	above
below	on	under

Look at the picture below. Circle the answer to each question.

Where is the cat?	inside the basket	outside the basket
Where is the dog?	above the table	below the table
Where is the bird?	inside the cage	outside the cage
Where is the cake?	under the table	on the table

GOAL

Learn to tell the time. A clock has two hands. The hour hand is short. The minute hand is long. The hour hand on this clock points to 3. The minute hand points to 12. That means the time is 3 o'clock.

3 o'clock

What time is shown on the clocks below?

☐ o'clock

☐ o'clock

☐ o'clock

☐ o'clock

Draw the hour hand on the clock to show two o'clock.

Remember: The hour hand is shorter than the minute hand.

1234567891234567891 2

> Practise using clocks. When you write the word *o'clock*, that means the minute hand on the clock is pointing to 12. The hour hand points to the hour number.

Draw the hour hand on the clocks below to show the time that is under the clock.

Remember: The hour hand is shorter than the minute hand.

5 o'clock

2 o'clock

9 o'clock

6 o'clock

This clock is missing four numbers. Write the missing numbers in their correct places on the clock.

Learn the concept of using money to buy items.

Draw a line from each toy to the dollars that match the price of the toy.

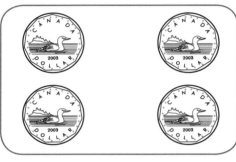

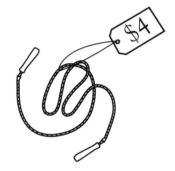

The price for a small jar of marbles is 3 dollars. The price for a large jar of marbles is 4 dollars. How many more dollars is the large jar?

Count the money

GOAL

Count coins to find the total amount of money.

Count the money in each pocket. Draw a line from each pocket to the correct amount written in the middle column.

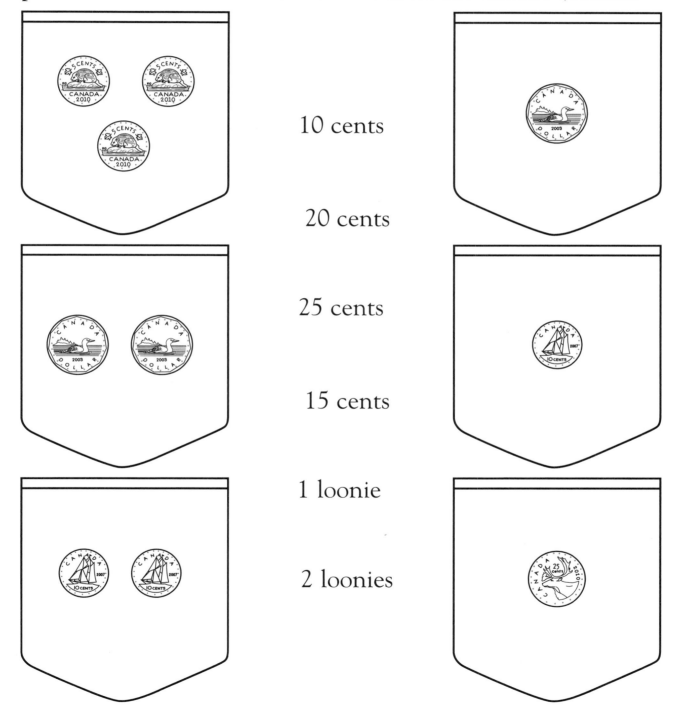

10 cents

20 cents

25 cents

15 cents

1 loonie

2 loonies

K Science

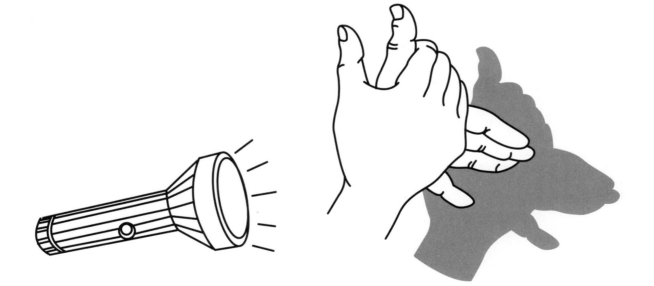

Note to parents

This section introduces science concepts to kindergarten children. The topics covered will be similar to the activities they encounter during kindergarten programs.

Contents
By working through this section, your child will practise:
- reading and writing;
- associating pictures and words;
- making observations about the world around him or her;
- categorizing animals and plants by type;
- recognizing habitats;
- finding the differences between types of plants and types of animals;
- performing experiments;
- describing the difference between a liquid and a solid;
- using positional words;
- noticing the weather;
- asking questions about what they see.

How to help your child
Young children at this age will not be able to read most of the instructions in this book. Therefore, there is an expectation that parents, guardians, or helpers will work closely with children as they progress through the book. Both parents/helpers and children can gain a great deal from working together.

Perhaps the most important thing you can do—both as you go through the workbook and in many everyday situations—is encourage children to be curious about the world around them. Whenever possible, ask them questions about what they see and hear. Ask them questions such as "Why?," "What if?," and "What do you think?" Always be positive about their answers. There is almost certainly a logic to their response, even if it is not correct. Explore and discuss their ideas with them.

Answers are found at the back of the book, along with further notes and tips for helping your child.

A garden is a small piece of land where flowers, fruits, and vegetables are grown. Some animals live in a garden, too.

Can you find the animals living in the garden? Point to each animal and name it. Describe animals that live in a garden near you.

A plant has many parts to help it grow.

Find each part of the plant and say its name.

This plant is a tulip.

The flower is where the seeds are made so that new plants can grow.

The stem of the tulip brings water to all the parts of the plant.

The leaves take in sunlight for the plant so it can make food.

The roots of the tulip grow in the ground and help the plant get water.

A tree is a large plant. The stem of a tree is made out of wood.

Touch each part of the tree and say its name.

This tree has many of the same parts as the tulip plant you saw on page 59.

The leaves take in sunlight for the plant so it can make food.

The branches of the tree stretch up to the sky so that the leaves can get lots of sunlight.

The stem of the tree is made of wood. It is called the trunk. The trunk brings water to all the parts of the plant.

The roots of the tree grow in the ground and help the tree get water.

Some trees lose their leaves in the fall and grow new leaves in the spring.

During the summer, trees have all their leaves. During the fall, the leaves of some trees fall to the ground. During the winter, you only see the branches of these trees. During the spring, the leaves grow back. Point to each tree and name the season it is in.

summer

fall

winter

spring

Many foods that we eat are plants.

Point to the two plants that we eat, and name them.

apple

tulip

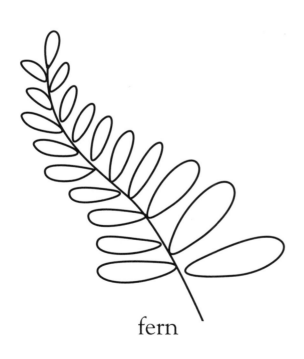

fern

tomato

Vegetables come from different parts of plants.

The roots of a plant grow in the ground and help the plant get water. Carrots and potatoes are root vegetables. The stem of the plant brings water to all the parts of the plant. Asparagus and celery are stems. The leaves take in sunlight for the plant so it can make food. Spinach and lettuce are leaf vegetables.

Point to each vegetable below, and say its name.
Is it a root, stem, or leaf vegetable?

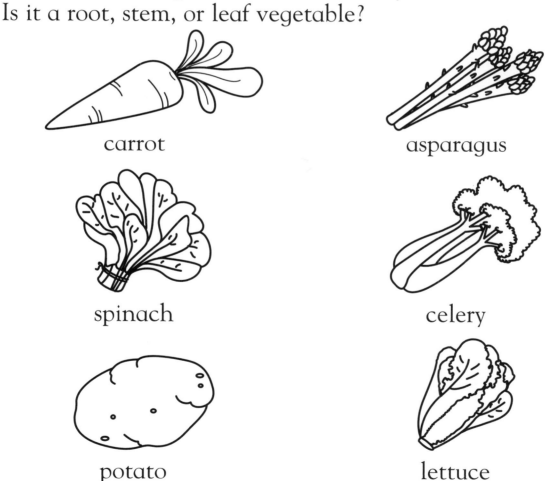

carrot

asparagus

spinach

celery

potato

lettuce

A fruit is the part of a plant that contains seeds.

Circle the fruit in each picture.

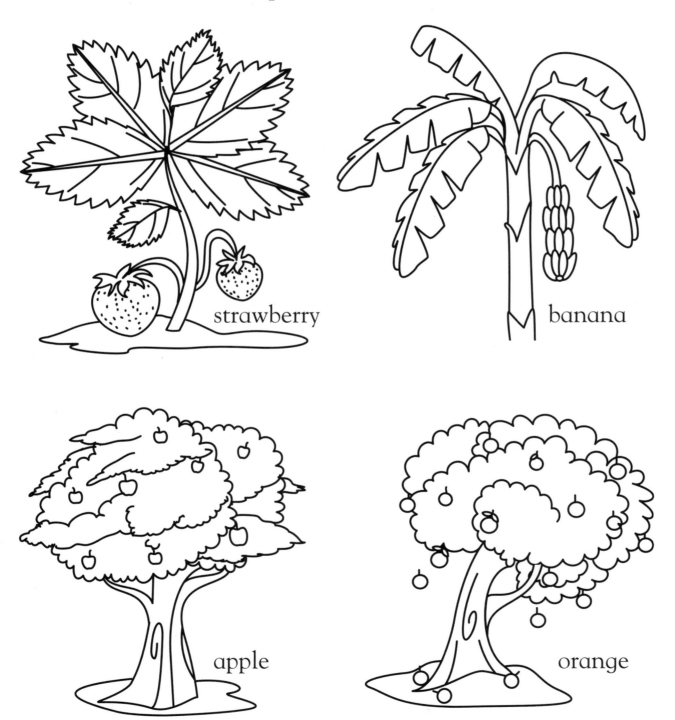

strawberry

banana

apple

orange

Many things we use are made from plants and trees.

Connect each plant with the things that are made from it.

This is a cotton plant. Many things that you wear are made from cotton. Socks and T-shirts are often made from cotton.

This is a tree. Many things you use every day are made from the wood of trees. Baseball bats and books are made from trees.

sock

book

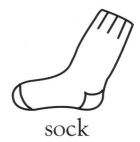

T-shirt

baseball bat

★ Plants and water

FACTS

Plants need water to grow.

TEST

What you need:

paper towel   2 plastic bags

water

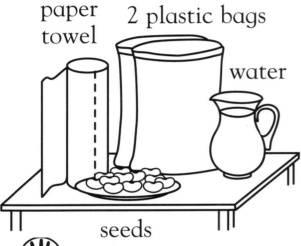

seeds

 What to do:

1. Place some bean seeds on a wet paper towel and fold it over. Place the paper towel in bag 1 and seal it.

2. Place some bean seeds on a dry paper towel and fold it over. Place the paper towel in bag 2 and seal it.

3. Put both bags in a warm, light place.

RESULT

After a week, open the bags. Describe what has happened to the seeds. Circle the picture that looks like the bag with water. Put an **X** on the picture that looks like the bag without water.

bag with wet seeds

bag with dry seeds

66

Plants need light to grow.

TEST

What you need:

two seedlings of the same type of plant of equal size

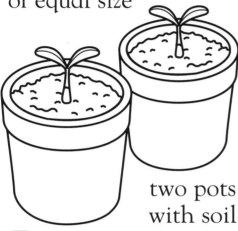

two pots with soil

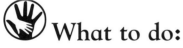 **What to do:**

1. Plant each seedling in a pot of soil.

2. Put one pot in a dark place.

3. Put the other pot in a sunny place.

4. Check the plants every day for one week and water them if necessary.

RESULT

Watch the growth of the plants for a week. Describe what has happened to the plants. Circle the picture that looks like the plant that got sun. Put an **X** on the picture of the plant that was in the dark.

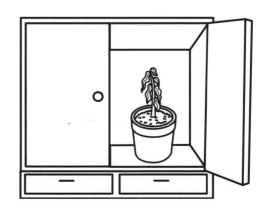

FACTS

Seeds need to travel to different places to grow new plants. They travel to find a place that has light and water.

Seeds travel in many ways. Match the seeds to the way they travel.

strawberry

acorn

dandelion

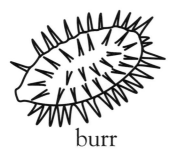

burr

These seeds have a parachute of fine hairs. They are carried by the wind.

The hooks of this seed stick to the fur of animals passing by.

These seeds are eaten with fruit, pass through the animal, and grow in a new place.

Squirrels bury these seeds to eat in the winter.

A habitat is a place where an animal or plant naturally lives or grows.

Draw a picture of of your home. Draw and name animals and plants that live and grow in and around your home. Make sure you include you and your family.

An ocean is a large body of water. Ocean water is salty. Many animals live in the ocean.

Draw a picture of an animal that lives in the ocean. Then colour the picture.

FACTS

A pond is a small body of fresh water.

Colour the animals and plants in this picture of a pond.
Can you name all the animals?

Some animals eat only plants. Some animals eat only other animals.

Circle all of the animals that eat only plants. Point to the animals that eat only other animals and say their names out loud.

cow

tiger

crocodile

beaver

horse

deer

Some animals eat both plants and animals.

Human beings eat both plants and animals. What do you like to eat? Draw your favourite food that comes from a plant in the **Plants** box. Draw your favourite food that comes from an animal in the **Animals** box.

What I like to eat

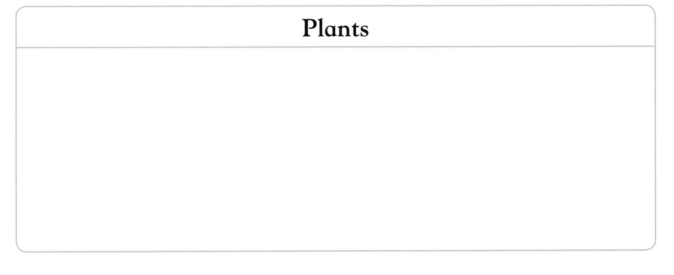

Plants

Animals

We see with our eyes.

Colour the eyes the same as yours. Then write your name beside the picture.

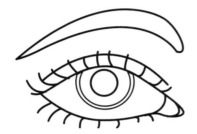 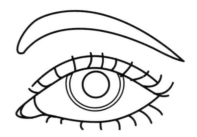

Draw the missing eyes on these animals.

FACTS

Hot and cold describe the temperature of something. Something that is hot has a high temperature. Something that is cold has a low temperature. A thermometer is used to measure how hot or cold something is.

Point to the pictures of the things that are hot.
Circle the pictures of the things that are cold.

snowman

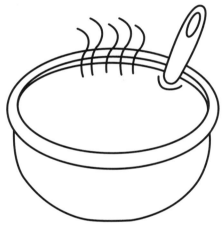

soup

ice cream

candle flame

ice water

fire

FACTS

We hear with our ears.

Circle the things you can hear with your ears.

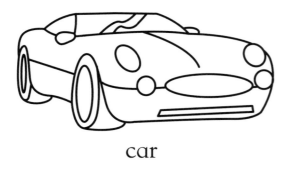

car

book

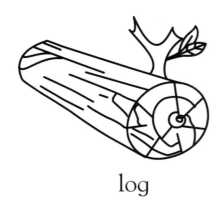

log

bell

cellphone

lamp

A noise can be loud or quiet. If you are close to a noise, it sounds loud. If you are far away from a noise, it sounds quiet.

The dog is barking. Which child hears the dog's bark the loudest? Colour that child's shirt red. Which child hears the dog's bark the quietest? Colour that child's shirt blue. Then colour the whole picture.

FACTS

We use our fingers to feel things. Our fingers tell us if things are hard, soft, rough, smooth, hot, or cold.

TEST **What you need:**

Gather up a variety of objects from around your house. The objects shown below will work well for this activity, but you can choose others if you like.

tennis ball

orange

wooden spoon

metal spoon

bagel

plastic bottle

 What to do:

1. Ask an adult to help you choose items from around the house.

2. Close your eyes and ask the adult to pass you something.

RESULT

Can you tell what you are holding?
Feel the object and describe it.

We use our nose to smell things.

Circle the things you can smell with your nose.

lemon

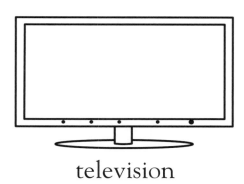

television

garbage

flower

spoon

skunk

The nose can detect many different smells.

TEST

What you need:

1 cup of lemon juice

1 cup of jam

1 cup of vinegar

1 cup of chopped banana

 What to do:

Close your eyes and ask an adult to pass you a cup to smell. What do you smell? Name the food you are smelling.

RESULT

Put an **X** next to the foods you identified correctly.

Jam	
Banana	
Vinegar	
Lemon juice	

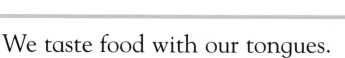

We taste food with our tongues.

Foods can taste sweet, salty, or sour. What do these foods taste like? Connect each food to its taste.

sweet

lemon

salty

candy

sour

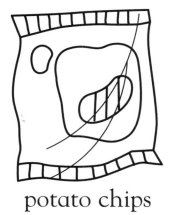

potato chips

Animals come in many shapes and sizes.

Animals move in different ways. Some animals walk and run. Some animals swim. Some animals fly. Animals that fly have wings. Circle each animal that has wings.

fly   cat

turtle   bat

bird

fish

Tame and wild animals

Some animals are wild. Other animals can be kept in a house. These animals are tame.

Circle the animals that are wild. Point to the animals that are tame and can be kept in a house.

dog

gorilla

fox

goldfish

hamster

lion

Tame animals can live in your home and be kept as pets.

Do you have a pet?

If you have a pet, what kind of animal is your pet?

What is your pet's name?

Do you have a friend who has a pet?

If you have a friend who has a pet, what kind of animal is that pet?

What is the name of your friend's pet?

Draw your favourite pet.

Pets need special care to keep them happy and healthy.

The pictures below show some of the things pets need to be happy and healthy. Point to the pictures of the things pets need and name them all. Can you think of anything else pets need?

food and water   exercise

home   medical care

home

food and water

exercise

medical care

Motion is how things move.

The words in the box describe some of the ways things move. Say the words aloud and point to the picture of the motion each word describes.

spin	slide	fall	fly	bounce	roll

bounce

roll

spin

slide

fly

fall

When you move something away from you, you push it.
When you move something closer to you, you pull it.

Look at each picture. Put an **X** in the box to say if the
movement shows pushing or pulling.

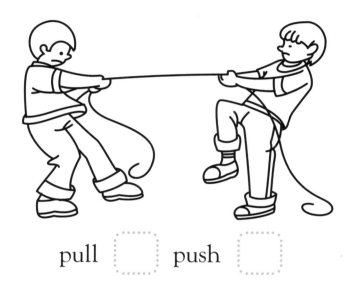

pull ☐ push ☐   pull ☐ push ☐

pull ☐ push ☐   pull ☐ push ☐

Light helps us to see.

Circle the things that generate light.

tree

campfire

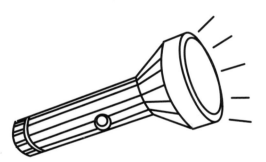

flashlight

sun

book

lamp

A shadow is a dark patch that forms where an object blocks out light.

TEST

What you need:

flashlight

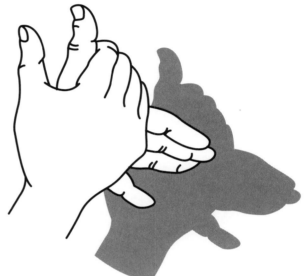

What to do:

1. In a dark room, turn on the flashlight and lay it on a table, pointing toward a wall.

2. Stand between the flashlight and the wall. Put your hands together, as shown above, to make the shadow of the dog.

3. What other shadows can you make on the wall?

RESULT

Can you explain what makes the shadow?

★ A rainbow

FACTS

A rainbow is an arch of colours that appears when the sun shines through rain.

Colour the rainbow.

Red
Orange
Yellow
Green
Blue
Indigo
Violet

You can make a rainbow by shining a light through water.

TEST **What you need:**

sheet of white paper, folded in half

clear glass half-filled with water

flashlight

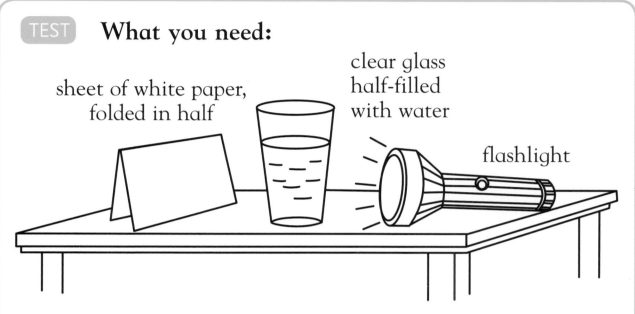

 What to do:

1. In a dark room, stand the paper a few inches behind the glass.

2. Turn on the flashlight and shine it through the water onto the paper.

RESULT

What happens? Draw what you see on the paper.

The things around you are solids, liquids, or gases.

Solid things keep their shape. Liquid things take the shape of the container they are in. Gases get bigger to fill the space they are in. Circle all the liquids. Point to the solids.

books

candy

juice

balloons

milk

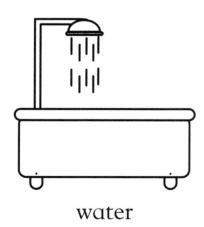

water

Air is a gas. Air is invisible but you can feel it and see that it is there by blowing bubbles.

TEST

What you need:

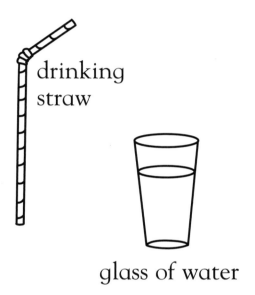

drinking straw

glass of water

 **What to do:**

1. Blow through the straw. Feel the air coming out of the other end with your hand.

2. Put the straw in the glass of water and blow.

RESULT

Draw what you see happening when you blow through the straw in the water. Why does this happen?

FACTS

You can fill a balloon with air.

What you need:

balloon

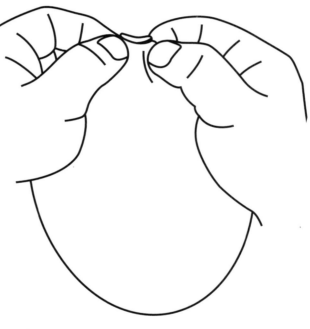

What to do:

1. Ask an adult to blow into a balloon and fill it with air.

2. Take the balloon in your fingers and hold the mouth firmly to keep the air in.

3. Stretch the mouth of the balloon. Can you hear the air make a squeaky noise as it escapes?

4. Now let go of the balloon.

RESULT

Describe what happened to the balloon. Why do you think this happened?

Wind is moving air.

Draw a circle around the things that use the wind.
Colour the picture.

Liquid takes the shape of the container it is in.

TEST

What you need:

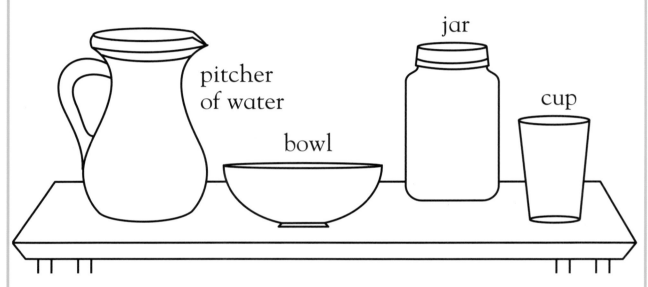

pitcher of water

bowl

jar

cup

 What to do:

1. Pour the water from the pitcher into a cup. See how the water fills the cup and becomes the same shape as the cup.

2. Now pour the water into a bowl. See how the water fills the bowl and becomes the same shape as the bowl.

RESULT

Describe what happens to the water when you pour it into different containers.

Bubbles are liquid filled with air.

TEST

What you need:

2 tablespoons of
dish soap

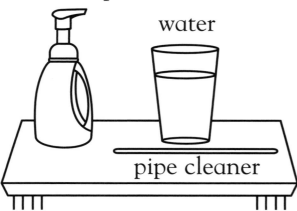

water

pipe cleaner

 What to do:

1. In a cup, mix together
   the dish soap and
   the water.

2. Bend the top of the pipe
   cleaner into a loop.

3. Dip the pipe cleaner into
   the bubble mixture and
   then blow into the loop
   to make bubbles.

RESULT

Draw what happens.

What is inside the bubbles?

Solids keep their shape.

Draw a line between each object and the shape it matches.

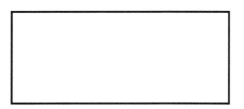

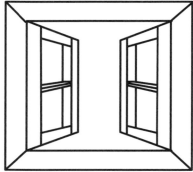

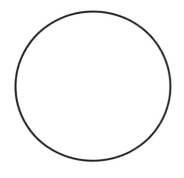

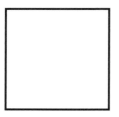

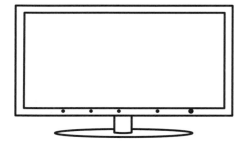

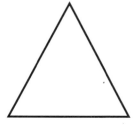

Water can be liquid or solid.

TEST

What you need:

bowl

water pitcher

ice-cube tray

 What to do:

1. Pour water into a pitcher. Is this water solid or liquid?

2. Pour the water from the pitcher into an ice-cube tray.

3. Put the ice-cube tray in the freezer for 5 hours.

4. Take the ice-cube tray out of the freezer and put the ice cubes in a bowl. Is the ice solid or liquid?

5. Keep the bowl of ice on a counter overnight. Look at the bowl in the morning.

RESULT

What happened to the water in the freezer?
What happened to the ice in the bowl?

What makes the water change between a solid and a liquid?

Freezing is when a liquid changes into a solid.
Freezing happens when it is very cold.

Look at the pictures. Circle the thing that will freeze in the cold.

juice   book   rain

puddle   car tire   ball

milk   baseball bat   soup

Melting is when a solid turns into a liquid.
Melting happens when it is very warm.

Draw a circle around the objects that melt when it is hot.

apple   book   chocolate

ball   ice cream   sneakers

snowman   hat   bread

K Spelling

Note to parents

This section introduces basic spelling skills to your child. The activities are intended to be completed by a child with adult support and will help your child's understanding of letters, words, and sentences.

Contents

By working through this section, your child will learn about:
- letters of the alphabet;
- upper-case and lower-case letters;
- vowels and consonants;
- long and short vowel sounds;
- consonant sounds;
- understanding the sequence of letters to learn words;
- initial, middle, and final sounds in consonant-vowel-consonant words;
- syllables;
- common sight words, such as "the," "of," "to," "you," "she," "my," "is," and "are";
- understanding print and learning to read sentences;
- reading kindergarten-level text with fluency, purpose, and understanding.

How to help your child

As you work through this section with your child, make sure he or she understands what each activity requires. Read the facts and instructions aloud. Encourage questions and reinforce observations that will build confidence and increase active participation in classes at school.

By working with your child, you will understand how he or she thinks and learns. When appropriate, use props such as pictures or flash cards to help your child visualize letters and words. If an activity seems too challenging, encourage your child to try another page.

Answers are found at the back of the book, along with further notes and tips for helping your child.

We spell words with letters. A set of these letters is called the alphabet. Each letter has a different shape and sound.

Read the letters of the alphabet aloud or sing them.

A a

apple

B b

ball

C c

cat

D d

door

E e

egg

F f

feet

G g

gate

H h

hen

I i

ice

J j

jar

K k
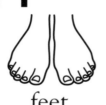
kite

L l

lamp

M m

mop

N n

nest

O o

octopus

P p

pencil

adwcSkfbomhqanwsCjgikeyZ

The alphabet has 26 letters. Each letter has an upper-case and a lower-case form.

Q q
queen

R r
rabbit

S s
sun

T t
turtle

U u
umbrella

V v
violin

W w
watch

X x
x-ray

Y y
yak

Z z
zipper

Write the letter that begins the name of each picture below.

_pple

_en

_est

FACTS

Activities using the alphabet help children identify, read, and write upper-case and lower-case letters.

Trace the upper-case and lower-case letters of the alphabet wherever they are missing.

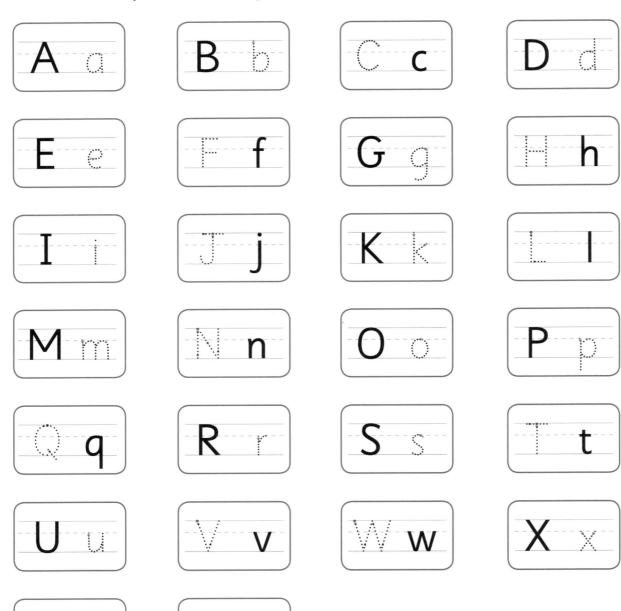

Matching the upper-case and lower-case letters of the alphabet helps children with reading and writing.

Draw a line from each sock on the top clothesline to the sock with the matching lower-case letter on the bottom clothesline.

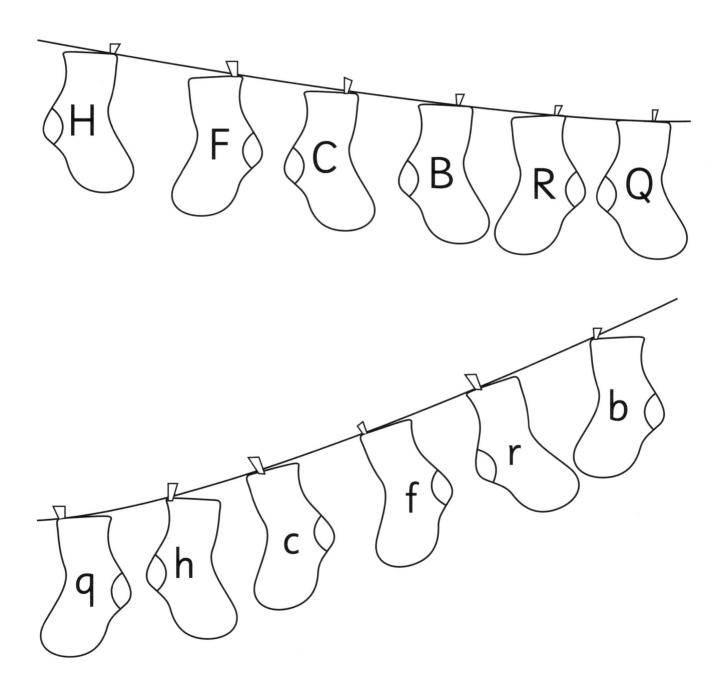

FACTS

Words are spelled with letters. Some letters are consonants and some are vowels. The letters **a**, **e**, **i**, **o**, and **u** are vowels. The letter **y** is sometimes a vowel and sometimes a consonant. The other letters of the alphabet are consonants.

Read each picture's name aloud. Circle the vowel you hear in the middle of each word.

sun	bed	hen	log

cat	pin	pup	wig

Look at each picture and write the consonant that begins the name of each picture.

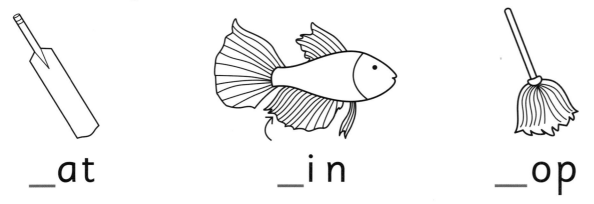

_at   _in   _op

Each letter has a different sound. For example, the letters **b-a-t** spell "bat." The letters **b-u-g** spell "bug."

Look at each picture and say its name aloud. Then write the letters of its name in the boxes in the correct order.

bat

bug

dig

dog

fin

fan

sun

sit

cup

cat

mat

mop

FACTS

The letter **b** begins the word "book." The letter **c** begins the word "cat." The letter **d** begins the word "duck." The letter **f** begins the word "fun."

Trace the upper-case and lower-case letters in each row. Circle the picture in each row whose name begins with the same letter.

Bb Bb Bb

leaf   bell

Cc Cc Cc

cup   pot

Dd Dd Dd

hen   dog

Ff Ff Ff

fan   net

The letter **g** begins the word "gift." The letter **h** begins the word "hut." The letter **j** begins the word "jump." The letter **k** begins the word "kite."

Trace the upper-case and lower-case letters in each row. Circle the picture in each row whose name begins with the same letter.

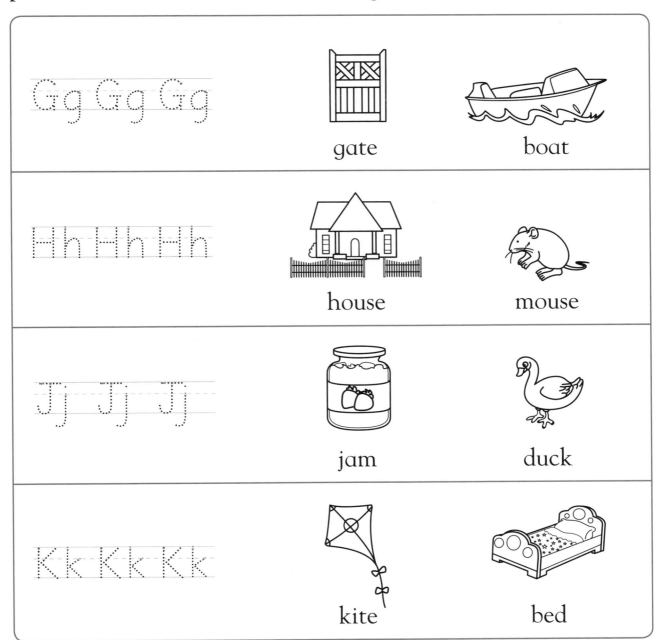

Gg Gg Gg   gate   boat

Hh Hh Hh   house   mouse

Jj Jj Jj   jam   duck

Kk Kk Kk   kite   bed

Consonants l, m, n, and p

FACTS

The letter **l** begins the word "lamp." The letter **m** begins the word "mop." The letter **n** begins the word "net." The letter **p** begins the word "pan."

Trace the upper-case and lower-case letters at the beginning of each row. Circle the two words in each row that begin with the same letter.

leaf   log   candle

mug   boot   moon

nurse   nest   swing

puppy   bat   pencil

FACTS

The letter **q** begins the word "quilt." The letter **r** begins the word "rabbit." The letter **s** begins the word "sock." The letter **t** begins the word "top."

Trace the upper-case and lower-case letters at the beginning of each row. Circle the two words in each row that begin with the same letter.

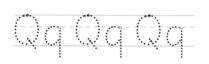 queen 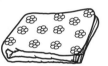 quilt cat

 robot door  rug

  soap  bus sun

  tiger  boat tent

The letter **v** begins the word "van." The letter **w** begins the word "window." The letter **x** begins the word "x-ray." The letter **y** begins the word "yard." The letter **z** begins the word "zebra."

Trace the upper-case and lower-case letters at the beginning of each row. Circle the word or words in each row that begin with the same letter.

Vv Vv Vv

van   pin   vase

Ww Ww Ww

worm   fan   window

Xx Xx Xx

x-ray   book   chick

Yy Yy Yy

yak   yogourt   shoe

Zz Zz Zz

zebra   zipper   sun

Words have different sounds based on the order of the letters they contain. If the beginning, middle, or final letters of a word change, a new word with a different sound is made.

Read each pair of words below. Then underline the letters that are different in each pair.

box   fox

pen   pan

coat   boat

rug   run

hen   ten

nail   pail

Beginning sounds

FACTS

Each letter in a word has a different sound. Identifying the initial sound of a word helps you to say it.

Read each picture's name on the left. Using a letter from the box, complete the rhyming picture's name on the right.

h	p	f

can   _an

bat   _at

cup   _up

fin   _in

pen   _en

116 adwcskfbomhganwscjgikeyz

FACTS

Recognizing simple consonant-vowel-consonant words builds knowledge of words, their sounds, and spellings.

Read each picture's name on the left. Using a vowel from the box, complete the picture's name on the right.

o	a	u

leg

l_g

hut

h_t

pin

p_n

cap

c_p

map

m_p

The ending sounds of words can be short or extended. Some letters produce short, or stop, sounds, such as the **t** in "bat." Other words end with exended, or continuous, letter sounds. For example, the letter **r** can be extended in "far."

Look at the first picture in each row. Read its name aloud. Look at the other two pictures in the row. Find the picture's name that ends in the same sound as the first picture's name. Circle that picture and its name.

man   web   run

bat   cat   dog

star   bell   car

Different letter sounds

Words can be broken up into letters and the sounds of the letters.

FACTS

Read the words aloud and write each letter in a separate box.

bug

hen

web

bus

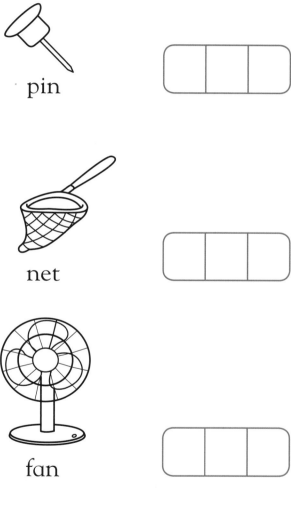

pin

net

fan

pup

FACTS

The long sound of the vowel **a** says its name. You hear the long "a" sound in the word "snake."

Read each picture's name aloud. Circle the names of the six pictures that have the long "a" sound. Make an **X** on the names of the two pictures that have the short "a" sound, as heard in "cat."

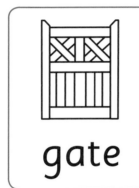

gate

whale

face

apple

cake

grapes

bat

train

Read the sentence below. Circle the two words that have the long "a" sound.

Owen and I like to play in the rain.

The long sound of the vowel **e** says its name. You hear the long "e" sound in the word "cheese."

Read each picture's name aloud. Circle the names of the six pictures that have the long "e" sound. Make an **X** on the names of the two pictures that have the short "e" sound, as heard in "pen."

key

bee

read

eagle

egg

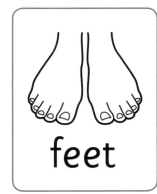

feet

bed

leaf

Fill in the letter **e** to complete the long "e" names of the bunny's body parts.

t__th   f__t

FACTS

The long sound of the vowel **i** says its name. You hear the long "i" sound in the word "lion."

Read each picture's name aloud. Circle the names of the six pictures that have the long "i" sound. Make an **X** on the names of the two pictures that have the short "i" sound, as heard in "tin."

ice

mice

pin

pipe

fish

kite

dice

iron

Read the sentence below. Circle the two words that have the long "i" sound.

The tiger is a big cat that has stripes.

The long sound of the vowel **o** says its name. You hear the long "o" sound in the word "boat."

Read each picture's name aloud. Circle the names of the six pictures that have the long "o" sound. Make an **X** on the names of the two pictures that have the short "o" sound, as heard in "pot."

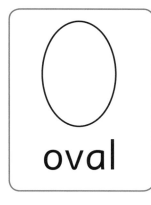

oval

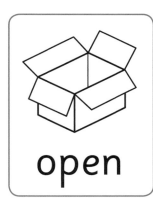

open

goat

mop

yogourt

log

toast

soap

Read the sentence below. Circle the two words that have the long "o" sound.

Jenny likes to eat yogourt and toast.

FACTS

The long sound of the vowel **u** says its name. You hear the long "u" sound in the word "cube."

Read the words on the balloons aloud. Colour the five balloons that have words with the long "u" sound. Make an **X** on the two balloons that have words with the short "u" sound, as heard in "fun."

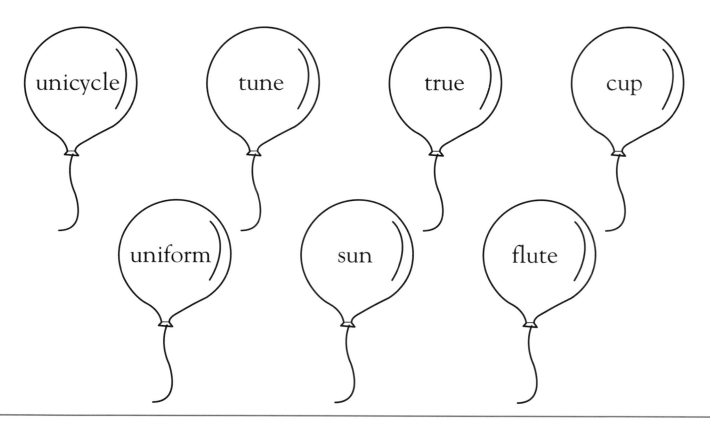

unicycle · tune · true · cup

uniform · sun · flute

Read the sentence below. Circle the three words that have the long "u" sound.

Brandon is using a tube of glue.

FACTS

The letter **y** can be tricky. Sometimes, it makes the long "e" vowel sound, as in the word "funny." Sometimes, it makes the long "i" vowel sound, as in the word "sky."

Circle the letter **y** in each word below. Read the word aloud. Listen to the "e" sound **y** makes in each word.

 puppy    bunny    lady

 happy   candy   baby

Write the letter **y** to complete each word below. Read the word aloud. Listen to the "i" sound **y** makes in each word.

 sk__   fl__    cr__

 fr__    b__e    sp__

FACTS

The word "apple" begins with the short sound of the vowel **a**. Some other words with the short "a" sound are "cat," "bag," and "rat."

Circle the names of the four pictures that have the short "a" sound. Make an **X** on the names of the two pictures that have the long "a" sound.

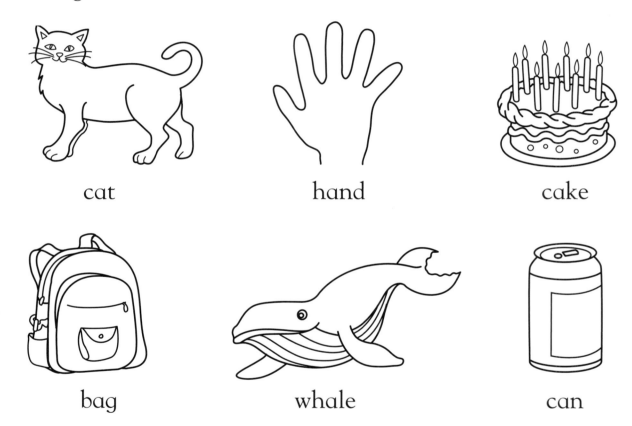

cat   hand   cake

bag   whale   can

For each word below, fill in the letter **a** to complete the word.

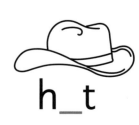

h_t    f_n   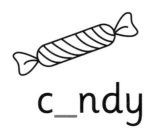 c_ndy

The word "egg" begins with the short sound of the vowel **e**. You also hear the short "**e**" sound in the words "jet," "desk," and "hen."

Read each picture's name in the word wheel aloud. Colour each section of the wheel in which the picture's name has the short "e" sound.

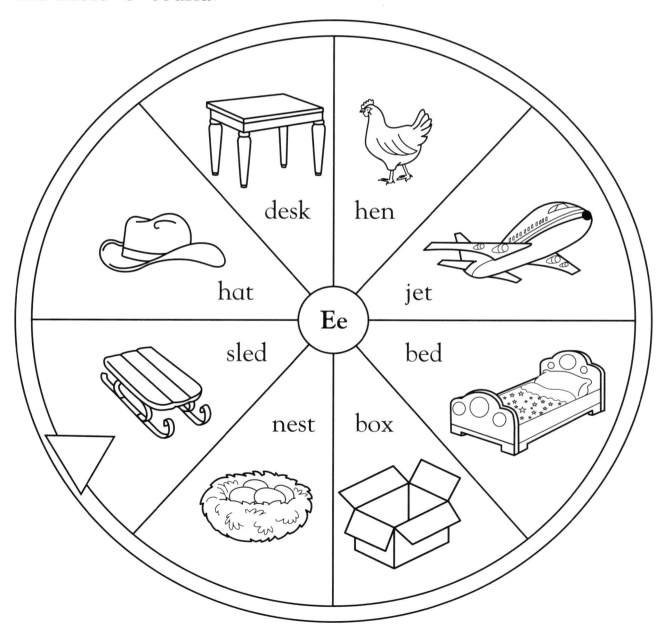

The short "i" sound

FACTS

The word "pin" has the short sound of the vowel **i**. You also hear the short "i" sound in the words "pig," "fin," and "fish."

Read each picture's name in the word wheel aloud.
If the word has the short "i" sound, underline the letter **i**.
Make an **X** on the words that have the long "i" sound.

a d w c s k f b o m h q a n w s c j g i k e y z

FACTS

The word "dog" has the short sound of the vowel **o**. You also hear the short "o" sound in the words "top" and "mop."

Read each picture's name aloud. Circle the six names that have the short "o" sound. Make an **X** on the two names that have the long "o" sound.

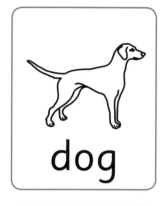

dog

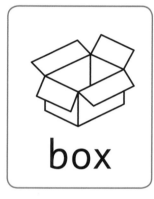

box

soap

mop

log

boat

fox

sock

Read the sentence below. Circle the three words that have the short "o" sound.

The dog jumped over a log to run after the frog.

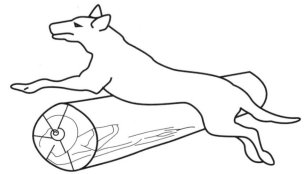

FACTS

The word "umbrella" has the short sound of the vowel **u**. You also hear the short "u" sound in the words "drum," "pup," and "sun."

Read each picture's name aloud. Circle the six names that have the short "u" sound. Make an **X** on the two names that have the long "u" sound.

drum

cup

unicorn

duck

sun

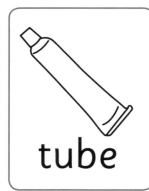

tube

jump

under

Read the sentence below. Circle the three words that have the short "u" sound.

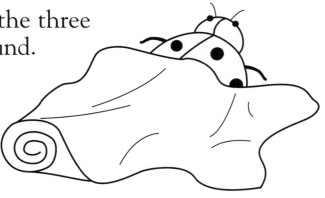

The bug is snug in the rug.

The individual letter sounds in simple words can be changed to make new words.

Read each picture's name on the left. Fill in the letter to complete the picture's name on the right.

 box

 __ox

 jet

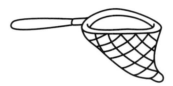 __et

 bug

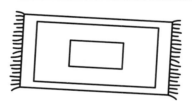 __ug

 hen

 __en

 cat

 __at

 fan

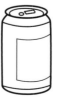 __an

FACTS

To identify spoken words, let your child listen to the beginning sounds of the words.

Look at the picture of each animal. Say the letter on the animal aloud. Then draw a line to match each animal to its name.

monkey

lion

fish

zebra

FACTS

Rhyming words have the same ending sound. For example, "cap" and "nap" end with the same letter sound.

Read the pictures' names in each box aloud. Circle "yes" if the words rhyme and "no" if the words do not rhyme.

cat	mat

yes   **no**

pan	can

yes   **no**

sun	box

yes   **no**

mop	top

yes   **no**

hat	bat

yes   **no**

jet	net

yes   **no**

pig	wig

yes   **no**

dig	pin

yes   **no**

Every word has one or more syllables, or beats. For example, the word "boat" has one syllable, the word "butter" has two syllables, and the word "dinosaur" has three syllables.

Read each animal's name aloud. As you say the word, count the number of its syllables. Circle the correct number.

lion

| 1 | 2 | 3 |

fish

| 1 | 2 | 3 |

horse

| 1 | 2 | 3 |

elephant

| 1 | 2 | 3 |

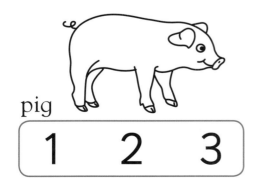

pig

| 1 | 2 | 3 |

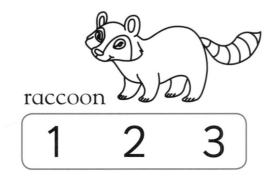

raccoon

| 1 | 2 | 3 |

Every syllable has one vowel sound. For example, the word "tomato" has three vowel sounds and three syllables.

Read each sentence aloud. Circle the number of syllables in each underlined word.

My snack today is a <u>banana</u>.

1   2   3

Do you have any <u>crayons</u>?

1   2   3

Turn off the <u>radio</u>.

1   2   3

Let's bake a <u>cake</u>.

1   2   3

Let's sit at the <u>table</u>.

1   2   3

I see an orange <u>butterfly</u>.

1   2   3

★ Sight words

FACTS

Sight words, or high-frequency words, are words commonly used in speaking and writing. The spelling of some of these words does not follow the usual letter-sound pattern.

Practise reading and using the sight words listed below.

all	four	on	too
am	get	please	under
are	good	ran	was
at	have	say	what
be	he	she	who
but	into	so	will
came	like	that	with
did	no	there	yes
do	now	they	you
eat	of	this	your

FACTS

Learning to spell and use sight words improves fluency in reading.

Read each sentence below. Circle the correct sight word to complete the sentence.

I know the days of has the week.

Do you your have a red crayon?

Does she her have a brother?

That girl be is my friend.

Kate went to am the zoo.

A cat is in so the tree.

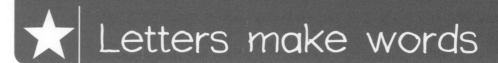

FACTS

Words are made with letters that are placed in order from left to right.

Find the words from the word box in the rectangles below.
Each rectangle has three words hidden in it.
Circle the words and read them aloud.

bat	cat	milk	rat	dog
drum	doll	plum	apple	

Food Words

a p p l e g o j p l u m q v m i l k

Toy Words

d o l l r j h i b a t x d r u m x

Animal Words

c a t j z p r a t g u l d o g s e

Print, or written text, is made up of letters and words that are read from left to right.

Read the words in each sentence aloud. Circle the word at the end of each line.

I see a bed.

I see a tree.

I see a horse.

I see a jar.

I see a kite.

Words in a sentence are read from left to right. At the end of a line, you return to the left side of the next line to continue reading.

Draw a line from the word in the box to the same word on the right.

 James has a ball .

ball

The dog is on the chair . chair

 Sara has a flower .

flower

The bird is in a nest . nest

 Kim has a book .

book

Words are combined to form sentences. The words in a sentence are separated by a single space between each word.

The sentences below tell a story. Count the words in each sentence. Circle the number of words each sentence contains.

I have a bear.

| 1 | 2 | 3 | 4 | 5 | 6 | 7 |

It is a brown bear.

| 1 | 2 | 3 | 4 | 5 | 6 | 7 |

It is not a big bear.

| 1 | 2 | 3 | 4 | 5 | 6 | 7 |

The little bear sits in a chair.

| 1 | 2 | 3 | 4 | 5 | 6 | 7 |

My little bear is a teddy bear.

| 1 | 2 | 3 | 4 | 5 | 6 | 7 |

Each sentence ends with a punctuation mark, such as a period (.).

Look at each sentence below. There is a space between each word in a sentence. Add a period at the end of each sentence. Read the sentence aloud.

 I can jump

 I like swings

 My cat is asleep

 I can fly a kite

A sentence is a group of words that expresses a complete thought. Sentences can be long or short.

Read each sentence aloud. Count the words in each sentence and circle the correct number.

I like ice cream.

1   2   3   4   5   6

I like vanilla ice cream.

1   2   3   4   5   6

I like strawberry ice cream, too.

1   2   3   4   5   6

I also like rainbow sprinkles.

1   2   3   4   5   6

Complete the sentence below.

My favourite flavour of ice cream is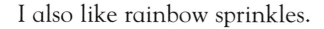

Count the words above. Write the number.

Sentences that end with rhyming words are called rhyming sentences. Some poems have rhyming sentences.

Read each sentence aloud. Look at each picture and pick the correct word to complete the rhyme.

The dog has a toy mouse.

The dog is in a ....

house   hut

The boy has a pet duck.

The duck sat
in the ....

wagon   truck

The pig lives in a pen.

The pig is named ....

Bob   Ben

Kate saw a ladybug.

The ladybug was
on a ....

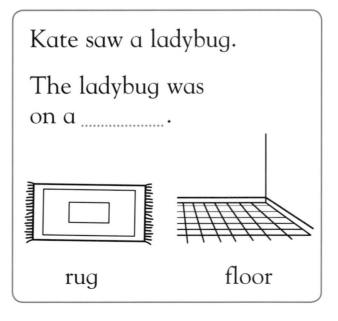

rug   floor

FACTS

You read words from left to right, top to bottom, and then page by page.

The pictures in the boxes below tell a story. Follow the numbers to read the story and answer the questions.

 1

The puppy barks.

2

The puppy is given food.

 3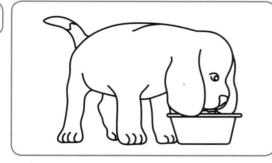

The puppy eats her food.

4

Finally, the puppy sleeps.

In which picture does the puppy bark?

In which picture does the puppy eat?

In which picture does the puppy sleep?

In which picture is the puppy given food?

FACTS

Knowing the sounds that letters make helps children recognize words and builds reading skills.

Read the story aloud. Circle the correct word to answer each question.

A Puppy Named Pooky

Joey has a little puppy.
She is a funny puppy.
The puppy is named Pooky.
One day, Pooky went to hide.
Where are you, Pooky?
Pooky was under the table.

What is the story about?

a cat   a puppy

Is the puppy big or little?

big   little

What is the name of the puppy?

Joey   Pooky

Where was Pooky hiding?

under the table   under the bed

Children should be able to read with purpose and understanding. Regular reading reinforces fluency so that children read accurately, quickly, and with expression.

Read all about the life of a frog in the four boxes.
Pick the correct word to complete each sentence below.

The Life of a Frog

1. "Ribbit!" That may be a frog calling. Let's visit the pond. Frogs live on land and in water.

2. Many frogs eat insects. They use their long tongues to catch them.

3. Frogs have long, strong back legs. They are good jumpers and swimmers.

4. Frogs lay eggs. The eggs hatch into tadpoles. The tadpoles grow up to be frogs.

Frogs live on land and in _____.　　water　　caves

Many frogs eat _____.　　insects　　fish

Frogs have long back _____.　　tails　　legs

Frogs are good _____.　　jumpers　　crawlers

K Language Arts

Note to parents

This section will help your child build kindergarten literacy skills. The activities are intended for a child to complete with adult support. Some concepts are just introduced to your child in a few activities. Your child will become more familiar with these concepts in the next grade.

Contents
By working through this section, your child will learn about:
- writing the letters of the alphabet;
- upper-case and lower-case letters;
- short vowel sounds;
- consonant blends;
- sight words;
- rhyming words;
- sound-alike words;
- ordering events;
- forming plurals with -s;
- nouns, verbs, and adjectives;
- question words;
- story characters;
- story settings;
- text features;
- reading for personal enjoyment.

How to help your child
On each page, read the facts and instructions aloud. Provide support while your child completes the activity. Encourage questions and reinforce observations to build confidence and increase participation at school.

Throughout the workbook, children will learn how to decode short consonant-vowel-consonant words. This will help them recognize these words as they read and later on help them with longer words, too.

As you work through the pages, help your child connect the content to specific personal experiences. For example, as you read a book together, explore the book cover. Ask your child to retell a story you have read, using words such as "first," "next," "then," and "finally." Practise writing skills by writing short letters to family and friends or by labelling pictures your child has drawn.

Be sure to praise progress made as a page is completed, a correct answer is selected, or a thoughtful response is given. This will help build the child's confidence and enjoyment in learning.

Answers are found at the back of the book, along with further notes and tips for helping your child.

FACTS

Lower-case letters are the small letters.
The first letters of the alphabet are **a** through **n**.

Trace lower-case letters **a** through **n**.
Then write these letters in lower case on your own.

a a a a art	h h h h ham
b b b b bad	i i i i ill
c c c c cat	j j j j jet
d d d d dot	k k k k kit
e e e e egg	l l l l lot
f f f f fit	m m m m mad
g g g g get	n n n n not

The lower-case alphabet

> The letters in most words are in lower case.
> The last letters of the alphabet are **o** through **z**.

Trace lower-case letters **o** through **z**.
Then write these letters in lower case on your own.

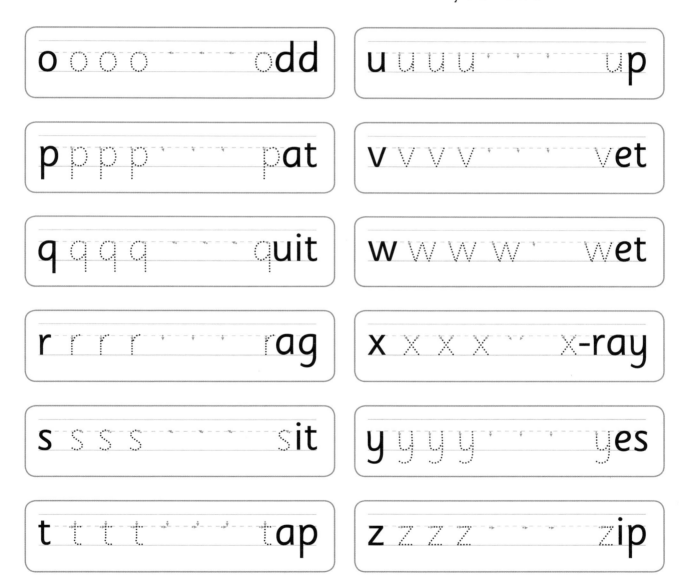

o o o o ⋯ odd	u u u u ⋯ up
p p p p ⋯ pat	v v v v ⋯ vet
q q q q ⋯ quit	w w w w ⋯ wet
r r r r ⋯ rag	x x x x ⋯ x-ray
s s s s ⋯ sit	y y y y ⋯ yes
t t t t ⋯ tap	z z z z ⋯ zip

Can you think of some words beginning with
the letters **a** through **z**?

dwcskfbomhqanwscjgikeyz

FACTS

Upper-case letters are used in the names of people, places, or events. These are the letters **A** through **N** in upper case.

Practise writing the upper-case letters. First trace the letters. Then write upper-case letters **A** through **N** on your own.

A A A   April

B B B   Brad

C C C   Cody

D D D   Dan

E E E   Emma

F F F   Fred

G G G   Grace

H H H   Hannah

I I I I   Ivan

J J J   Joe

K K K   Kim

L L L   Logan

M M M Morgan

N N N   Nora

The upper-case alphabet

Upper-case letters are used at the beginning of a sentence and in titles. Here are the letters **O** through **Z** in upper case.

FACTS

Practise writing the upper-case letters. First trace the letters. Then write upper-case letters **O** through **Z** on your own.

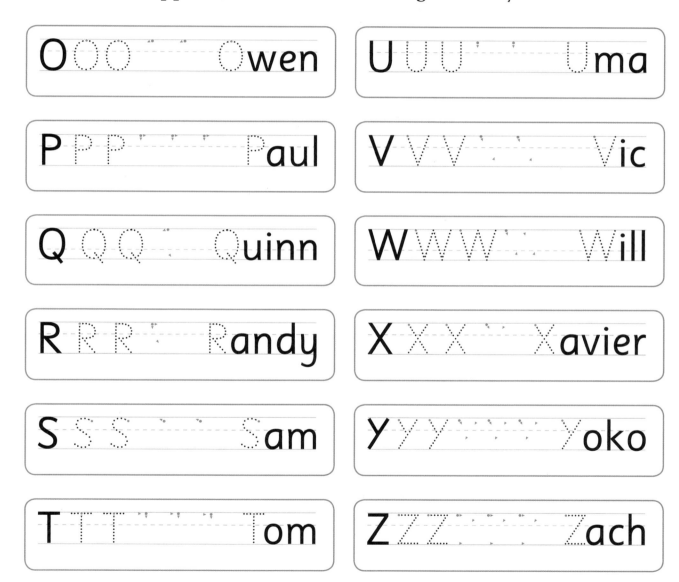

Can you think of some names beginning with the letters **A** through **Z**?

Books have covers. Covers give information about books.

Description	Instruction
The title is the name of the book.	Look at the book's cover. Draw a box around the title.
The author is the person who wrote the book.	Draw a line under the author's name.
A book title uses upper-case letters. People's names also start with upper-case letters.	Circle all the upper-case letters.
The title and picture on a book's cover can give you a clue as to what the book will be about.	What do you think you would read in this book? Finally, colour the book cover.

Silly Skunk
Stories

by **R**osy **S**niffin

Stories have a beginning, a middle, and an end.

Look at the pictures below. Then tell the story they show aloud. What happens first? What happens next? What happens last? When you have told the story, colour the pictures.

1.

....

....

2.

....

....

3.

....

....

4.

....

....

The letter **a** can sound like the **a** in "apple"
(short "a") or the **a** in "ape" (long "a").

Each word is missing its short "a." Write the letter
to complete the word. Then read each word aloud.

w_g

b_t

s_d

c_p

f_n

g_s

Two words that end in the same sound are called rhyming words. Rhyming words begin with different sounds.

Read the sentences aloud. Draw a line under the rhyming words.

My dad was mad.

A mat is flat.

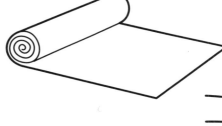

Put the rag in the bag.

The rat sat on the cap.

★ Rhyming match

Rhyming words often have similar spellings. Sometimes rhyming words can have completely different spellings.

Read each word aloud. Find the pairs of rhyming words in the balloons. Colour each pair the same colour.

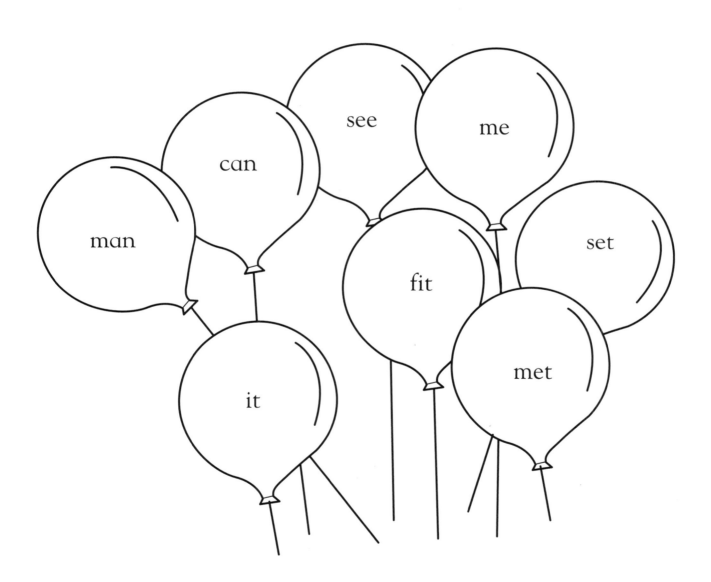

FACTS

A nursery rhyme is a poem or song for children.
Nursery rhymes are passed down through the years.

Read the nursery rhyme aloud. Underline the rhyming words.
Draw a picture that illustrates the nursery rhyme.

Hey, diddle, diddle,

The cat and the fiddle,

The cow jumped over the moon.

The little dog laughed

To see such sport,

And the dish ran away with the spoon.

Saying words aloud can make it easier to figure out if they rhyme. Here are some more rhyming words to practise.

Find the rhyming words. Draw a line between each pair.

book

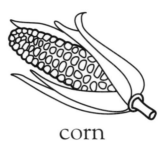

corn

clock

hook

horn

socks

fox

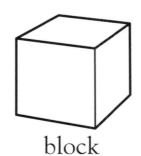

block

FACTS

Some words are used often in reading and writing.
You can learn to recognize these words.

Read the words aloud. Use them to complete sentences.

off	out	from	in	to	for

I gave the bag .... Bob.

The gift is .... you.

Jane took the book .... me.

The dog is .... the house.

We are .... of the car.

The lid is .... the pot.

A character is a person or animal in a story.

Read the story aloud.

A wolf liked to look at the stars. One night,
he walked along looking up at the stars.
He didn't see a hole in the ground and fell into it.
Another wolf passing by said, "You see the stars far
away. Why don't you see the ground under your feet?"

Below, circle the character that this story is about.

A setting is where and when a story takes place.

Read the story aloud.

> Jenny and Jack climbed on a sled. They zoomed
> down a hill. The winter air turned their cheeks cold.
> The sled stopped at the bottom of the hill.
> Jack said, "Let's ride again!"

Circle the picture that shows the setting of the story.

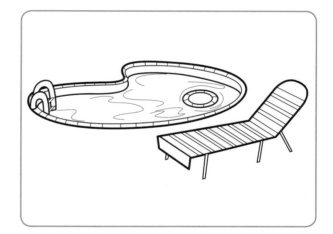

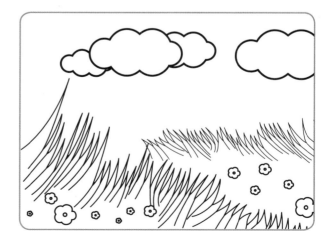

FACTS

The letter **e** can sound like the **e** in "egg" (short "e") or the **e** in "eel" (long "e").

Each word is missing its short "e." Write the letter to complete the word. Then read each word aloud.

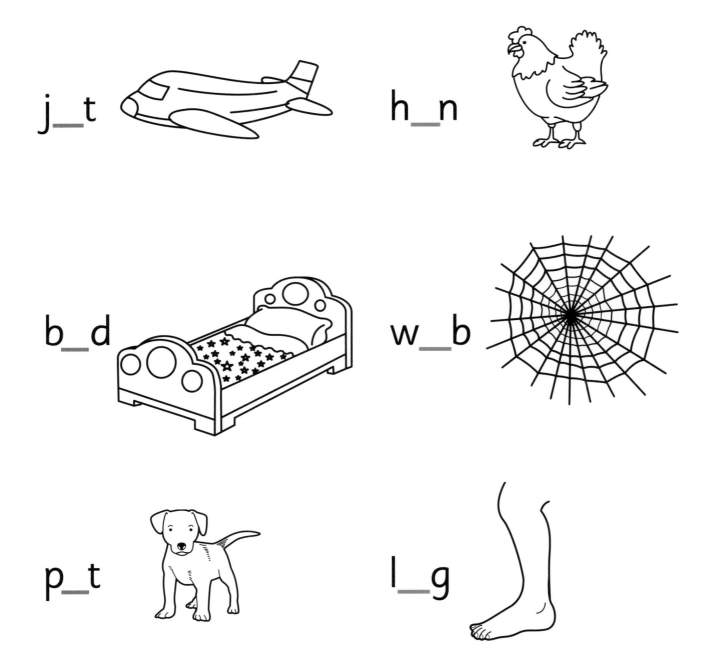

j_t

h_n

b_d

w_b

p_t

l_g

Rhyming words in a sentence make it more fun to read. Here are some more rhyming words.

Read the sentences aloud. Draw lines under the rhyming words.

I led the red hen.

She fed the wet pet.

A bird can rest in a nest.

Ten men saw the pen.

People read for different reasons.
Sometimes they read to learn.

Read the text below.

A map helps you find your way. A map can show
your home. It can show your school. A map can
show you how to go from your home to your school.

Circle the picture that shows what the text is about.

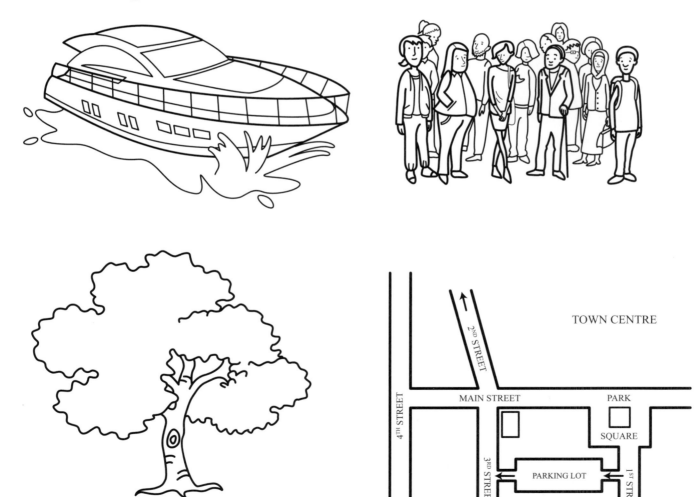

Labels ★

Labels are a text feature.
They give information about a picture.

Write labels naming the parts of the tiger.
Use the words from the word bank.

| back | ear | eye | leg | nose | tail |

FACTS

Some words name a person, a place, or a thing.

Circle the words that name a person, a place, or a thing.

bird

run

train

man

pull

leaf

car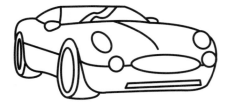

book

An action word names anything one can do or be.

Circle the action words.

sun

kick

jump

door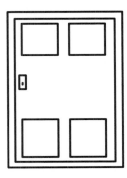

hide

sing

frog

hold

FACTS

The letter **i** can sound like the **i** in "big" (short "i") or the **i** in "ripe" (long "i").

Each word is missing its short "i." Write the letter to complete the word. Then read each word aloud.

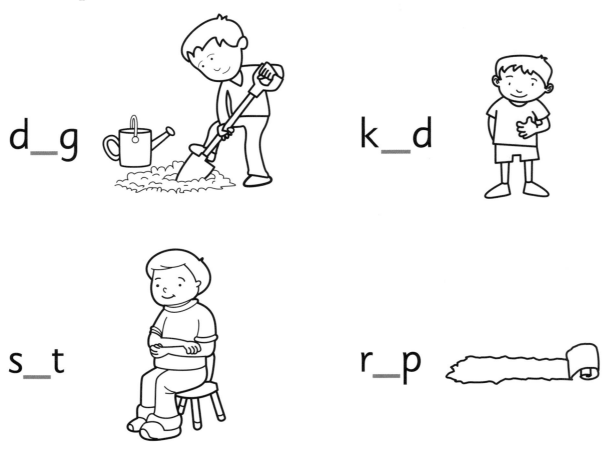

d_g

k_d

s_t

r_p

b_b

p_n

Rhyming words

> One way to create a word that rhymes with another word is to change the first letter of the word.

Make rhyming words using letters from the letter bank.

r	d	w	p	f	t

_in   _in

_id   _id

_ig   _ig

Some words describe people, places, or things.

Draw a line between the picture and the word that describes it.

funny

red

soft

loud

Telling or writing information in order helps it make sense.

This story is out of order. What happens first, next, and last? Write 1, 2, and 3 by the pictures to put them in the correct order.

FACTS

Make sense of information by telling
or writing it in order.

Read the text below. Then look at the pictures.
Number the pictures 1, 2, 3, and 4 to show
the order in which the story happened.

Meg wanted to sell lemonade. First, she made the lemonade.
Next, she set up her stand. Then, she hung up a sign.
Finally, Meg sold lots of lemonade to her friends!

The letter **o** can sound like the **o** in "dog" (short "o") or the **o** in "rope" (long "o").

Each word is missing its short "o." Write the letter to complete the word. Then read each word aloud.

p_t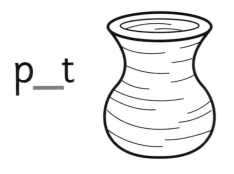

d_t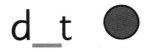

fr_g

s__ck

m_p

r_d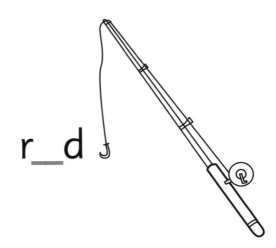

★ Rhyming words

FACTS

If words end with the same sound, they are rhyming words.

Read the sentences aloud. Circle the rhyming words.

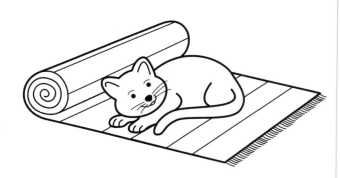

The cat sits on the mat.

Bob likes corn on the cob.

Lots of dogs sit on logs.

The pot is not too hot.

Words can name a general idea or topic, such as "place" or "job." Other words are more specific, such as "city" or "teacher."

Find the words that name foods in the spaces. Colour those spaces red. Find the words that name animals in the spaces. Colour those spaces green.

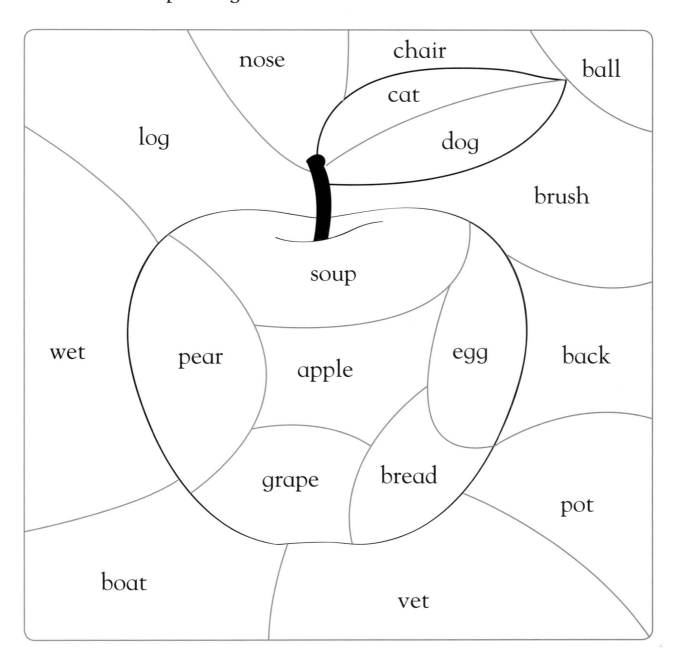

Singular means one. Plural means more than one. To make some words plural, add an **s** at the end of the word.

Make these words plural.

bat_

pig_

cane_

pan_

To make some words plural, add an **s** at the end of the word.

Make these words plural.

shoe_

clip_

dog_

sock_

My favourite storybook

A story has a title, or name. Stories are made up by authors. Stories also have characters and a setting.

Find one of your favourite storybooks to read together. Write down the title, author, characters, and setting of the story. Write down why you like it.

My favourite storybook

Title: ....

Author: ....

Characters: ....

Setting: ....

Why I like this book: ....

....

Draw a picture of something that happens in your favourite storybook.

Some books are about true events. Some books inform us about a subject.

Find a favourite book that is about true events to read together. Write down the title, author, and subject of the book. Write down why you like it.

My favourite true book

Title: ....

Author: ....

Subject: ....

Why I like this book: ....

....

....

Draw a picture of what your favourite true book is about.

FACTS

The letter **u** can sound like the **u** in "up" (short "u") or the **u** in "use" (long "u").

Each word is missing its short "u." Write the letter to complete the word. Then read each word aloud.

r_g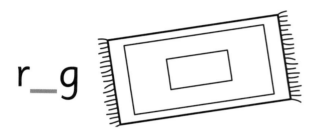

b_d

h_t

c_b

b_s

p_p

Using a rhyme in a sentence can make it easier to remember.

Read the sentences aloud. Draw lines under the rhyming words.

It is fun to run.

Can you cut a nut?

A bug is on the mug.

The fox is in the box.

FACTS

Some words sound alike but are spelled differently.

Read each pair of words aloud. They sound alike!
Trace the letters that change the spelling of the words.

te a   te e

s o n   s u n

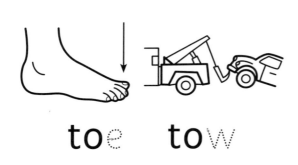

to e   to w

Fairy Tale

ta il   ta le

ha ir   ha re

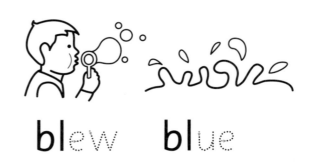

bl ew   bl ue

This popular song names different parts of the body.

Sing or say the song. As you sing, point to the parts named.
Then use words from the song to label the parts of the body.

Head, shoulders, knees and toes, knees and toes.
Head, shoulders, knees and toes, knees and toes.
And eyes, and ears and mouth and nose.
Head, shoulders, knees, and toes, knees and toes.

★ | Question words

Question words help people think about and understand what they read, do, or see.

The animals are running a race in the park. Look at the picture. Then answer the questions.

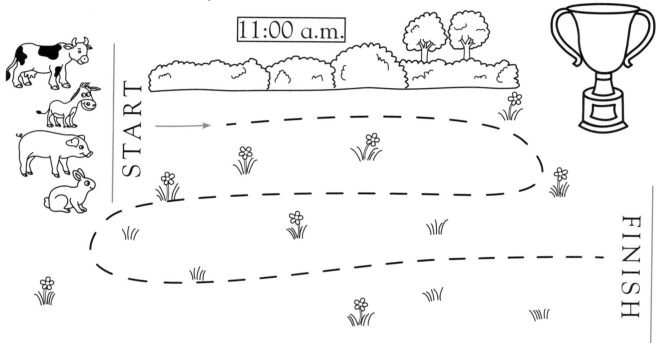

Who is running the race? Circle the answer in the picture.

What will the winner of the race get? Draw a box around it.

Where will the runners go? Trace the answer with your pencil.

When is the race? Circle the answer.

Why do you think the race is in a park? Talk about your ideas.

How will the runners know where to go? Draw a box around the answer.

Question words are words that help people ask for information.

Select question words from the word bank to best complete each question.

who	what	where	when	why	how

.... do you tie a shoe?

.... is at the door?

.... are there clouds in the sky?

.... is my dog?

.... will we eat dinner?

.... time is it?

FACTS

Letters are used together to make new sounds.

Trace the letters to complete each word. Say the words aloud.

bl**ock**

gl**ue**

cl**ips**

gr**apes**

br**ush**

cr**ab**

Certain letters make special sounds when they are used together.

c + h makes the sound that starts the word "chip."
s + h makes the sound that starts the word "sheep."
t + h makes the sound that starts the word "thin."
Draw a line to connect each word to its sound.

shoes

chair

th

cheese

sh

think

three

ch

ship

Sometimes one word has more than one meaning.

Use the words in the word bank to write the names of the pictures. The first one has been done for you.

| box | duck | fall | train |

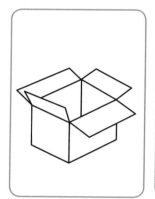

train

......

....

FACTS

Every letter has an upper-case and a lower-case form.

For each letter, fill in the missing upper-case
or lower-case letter.

.... a   B ....   C .... d

.... e   .... f   .... g   H ....

I .... j   K ....   L ....

.... m   .... n   .... o   P ....

.... q   .... r   .... s   T ....

.... u   V .... w   X ....

.... y   Z ....

Some words are easy to recognize.
Others need to be sounded out.

Say the words describing these pictures aloud.
Then write the words.

....

....

....

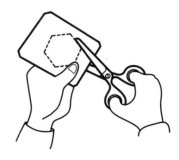

....

....

....

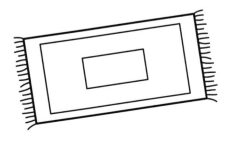

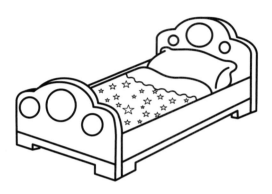

....

....

....

People can share ideas and give information through writing.

Complete the sentences to describe your day.

My day

My name is ....

Here is what happened to me today/yesterday. (Circle one.)

First, ...

....

Then, ...

....

Finally, ...

....

I felt ....

.... !

Certificate

Congratulations to

....

for successfully
finishing this book.

GOOD JOB!

You're a star.

Date

....

Answer section
with parents' notes

This section provides answers to all the activities in the book and will enable you to mark your children's work. Notes for each page explain common errors, and in some cases provide additional activities to help reinforce learning.

⭐ **Count 1 to 5**

GOAL
Practise counting from 1 to 5.

1 2 3 4 5

How many stars are there in each row?
Circle the correct number.

★★   (2) 3 4

★★★★   2 3 (4)

★★★   1 2 (3)

★★★★★   3 4 (5)

Write the two missing numbers on each line.

1   2   [3]   4   [5]

[1]   2   3   [4]   5

1   [2]   3   4   [5]

Let children count as they place a finger on each star. Then ask them to write the number under or on each star as they count, which will help reinforce their counting skills.

Count 6 to 10 ⭐

GOAL
Practise counting from 6 to 10.

6 7 8 9 10

How many apples are there in each row?
Circle the correct number.

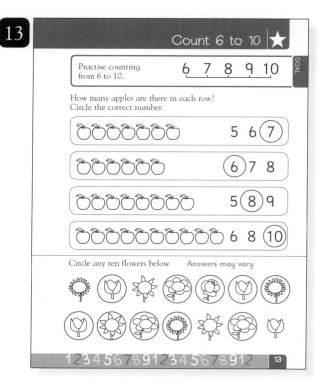

5 6 (7)

(6) 7 8

5 (8) 9

6 8 (10)

Circle any ten flowers below.   *Answers may vary*

Many children enjoy learning while touching or moving objects. Extend the activity on this page by providing cut-out paper apples that can be counted along with each row of apples on the page.

⭐ **Count up to 10**

GOAL
Practise counting up to 10.

5 6 7 8 9 10

How many objects are there in each box?
Write the correct number.

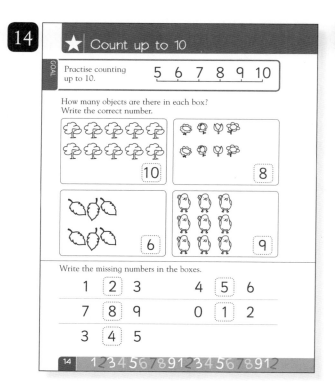

[10]   [8]

[6]   [9]

Write the missing numbers in the boxes.

1   [2]   3   4   [5]   6

7   [8]   9   0   [1]   2

3   [4]   5

To reinforce counting in groups, arrange ten coins into various groups. Let children practise counting the coins in each group, followed by adding up the numbers to find the total number of coins.

Count up to 10 ⭐

GOAL
Practise counting up to 10.

5 6 7 8 9 10

Look at the ten houses along the trail. Write the numbers that are missing in the circle next to each house.

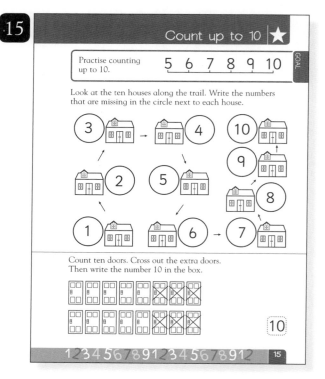

Count ten doors. Cross out the extra doors.
Then write the number 10 in the box.

[10]

Children will have fun following the trail as they count and write the missing numbers. Point to the numbers and explain that numbers increase by one on each step of the trail.

16

★ | What makes 10?

GOAL | Add different numbers from 1 to 9 to make 10.

Count each group of toys. Write the correct number of toys in the box.

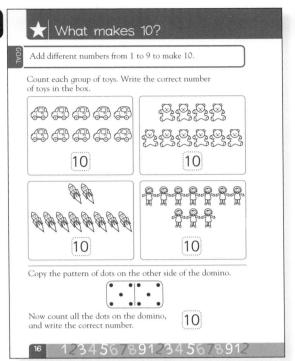

10

10

10

10

Copy the pattern of dots on the other side of the domino.

Now count all the dots on the domino, and write the correct number. | 10

16 1234567891234567891

Encourage children to look for patterns to help them determine quantities and gain confidence in their math skills. For example, five and five should become instantly recognizable as ten. Let them move objects to match the patterns on the page.

17

Practise making 10 ★

GOAL | Review how to make 10.

Write the numbers from 1 to 10 in the circles next to each car on the path below.

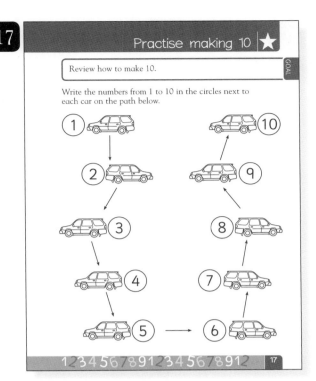

1234567891234567891 17

Learning what makes ten is key to understanding our number system. Try the following exercise: Cut out ten circles. Label each circle with a number and a corresponding series of dots. Have children practise selecting groups of circles that make ten.

★ | Sets of 10

GOAL | Learn about making sets of 10.

Count the objects in each box. Add the correct number to make 10.

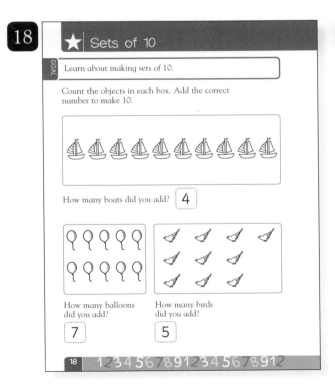

How many boats did you add? | 4

How many balloons did you add? | 7

How many birds did you add? | 5

18 1234567891234567891

Draw a row of ten squares. Number each square from 1 to 10, and let children see and count the numbers. Then cut out ten cardboard circles, and let children arrange them in groups to see how many ways they can make ten—two groups of five, a group of four and one group of six, five groups of two and so on.

19

Ways to make 10 ★

GOAL | Review ways to make 10.

Draw the number of objects to make 10. The first one has been done for you

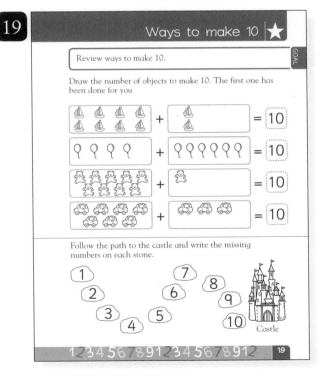

+ | = 10

+ | = 10

+ | = 10

+ | = 10

Follow the path to the castle and write the missing numbers on each stone.

1
2
3
4
5
6
7
8
9
10
Castle

1234567891234567891 19

Have fun playing a game: Create a set of ten cards, and number them 1 through 10. Create another set of ten cards, but this time use star stickers to represent the numbers. Let children match each number card with its corresponding star-sticker card.

★ Recognize shapes

Learn that objects have shapes, and shapes have names.

Look at the objects. Circle the correct shape of the object in each row.

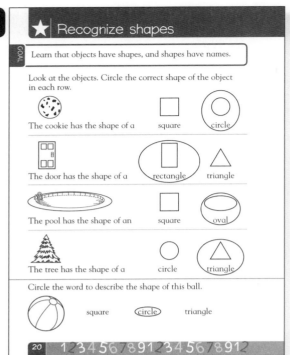

The cookie has the shape of a ··· square ··· (circle)

The door has the shape of a ··· (rectangle) ··· triangle

The pool has the shape of an ··· square ··· (oval)

The tree has the shape of a ··· circle ··· (triangle)

Circle the word to describe the shape of this ball.

square ··· (circle) ··· triangle

Help children identify shapes. After reading a picture book, review the pages and point out circles, squares, and triangles in the illustrations. Take turns as you look at each page to see how many shapes you can find in each scene.

Different shapes ★

Learn to identify different shapes.

Look at the shapes in each row. Circle the shape that is different.

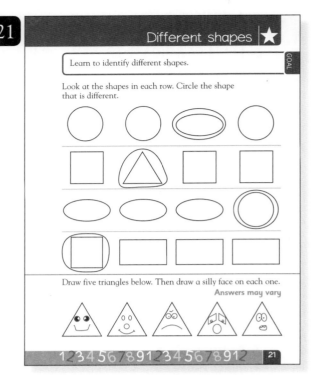

Draw five triangles below. Then draw a silly face on each one.

Answers may vary

Reinforce problem-solving skills in creative ways. After baking a pan of brownies, let children help decide how you will cut them up. Let your child estimate how many servings of brownies you can cut.

★ Describe shapes

Describe shapes by the number of sides and corners.

Circle the word that correctly completes each sentence.

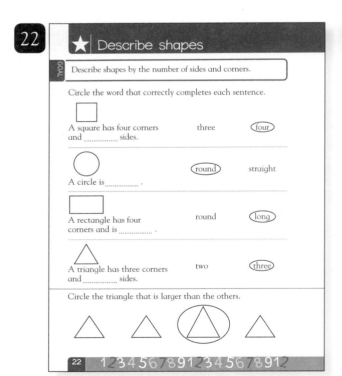

A square has four corners and .... sides. ··· three ··· (four)

A circle is .... ··· (round) ··· straight

A rectangle has four corners and is .... ··· round ··· (long)

A triangle has three corners and .... sides. ··· two ··· (three)

Circle the triangle that is larger than the others.

Make a simple jigsaw puzzle to reinforce shapes: Cut up the front of an old cereal box or an old greeting card into circles, squares, triangles, and rectangles. Engage children in describing the shapes as they work to put the puzzle together.

Compare shapes ★

Shapes can vary in size. Learn to find the shapes that are larger.

Look at the shapes in each box. Colour in the largest shape.

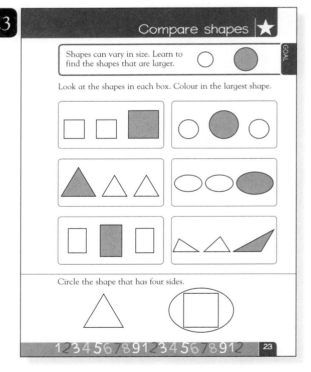

Circle the shape that has four sides.

Cut scrap paper into a variety of shapes and sizes. Guide children in sorting the paper first by shapes, and then into size order. You can provide plastic containers for easy sorting.

★ Create shapes

Learn to draw shapes.

Look at each shape and make it into an object.

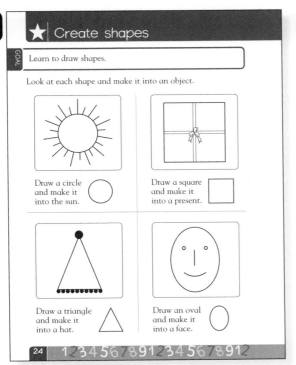

Draw a circle and make it into the sun.

Draw a square and make it into a present.

Draw a triangle and make it into a hat.

Draw an oval and make it into a face.

Encourage shape skills and tactile learning with colourful clay: Provide children with four lumps of coloured clay. Ask them to form a circle, a square, a triangle, and an oval using the clay.

More shapes ★

Practise finding and counting shapes.

Colour the circles red. ◯ Colour the rectangles yellow. ▭
Colour the squares blue. ☐ Colour the triangles green. △

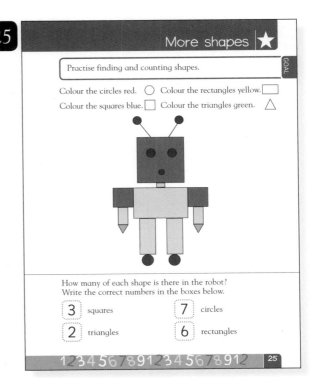

How many of each shape is there in the robot?
Write the correct numbers in the boxes below.

3 squares   7 circles

2 triangles   6 rectangles

Guide children in using the key. Colour each shape in the key to illustrate how they should colour the shapes on the robot. Review as they begin to colour to check their understanding.

★ Shape patterns

Learn to draw shapes and continue patterns.
Patterns are repeated sets of objects.

Draw the shape to continue the pattern in each row.

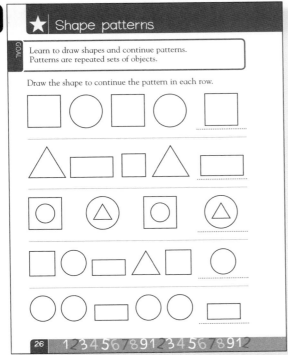

To extend their knowledge of shapes, ask children to draw a picture of their room, a toy, or the playground. Encourage them to use shapes in their drawing. Review their drawings, and ask them to point to and name the shapes.

More patterns ★

Practise continuing patterns.

Look at the cupcakes below. In each row, follow the pattern and decorate the tops of the undecorated cupcakes with the correct design.

Look at the pattern of the cookies below. Draw two more cookies to continue the pattern.

Have fun and reinforce math skills by using stickers. Start a simple pattern and let them continue it. Then have them create a pattern of either the shapes or colours of the stickers.

★ The same

Which has the same? ★

GOAL Learn to identify objects that are the same.

Look at each row of animals. Circle the two animals that are the same.

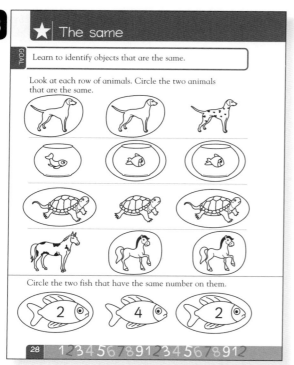

Circle the two fish that have the same number on them.

GOAL Learn to compare characteristics, such as numbers and letters.

Put the balls into the correct boxes: Draw a line from each ball with a number on it to the number box. Draw a line from each ball with a letter on it to the letter box.

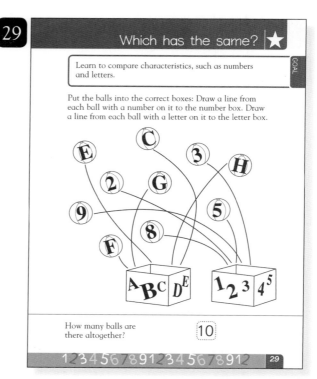

How many balls are there altogether?   10

Reinforce accuracy of numbers. Write the numbers from 1 to 10 on scraps of paper. Include four numbers that are written incorrectly, backward, or missing a part. Ask children to find the numbers that are not correct.

Many children need help determining the difference between letters and numbers, and the difference between numbers and letters that look similar—6 and 9, 1 and 7, E and F, and so on. The activity on this page will reinforce those skills.

★ Not the same

Which is different? ★

GOAL Learn to find things that are not the same, or different.

Circle the leaf in each row that is different.

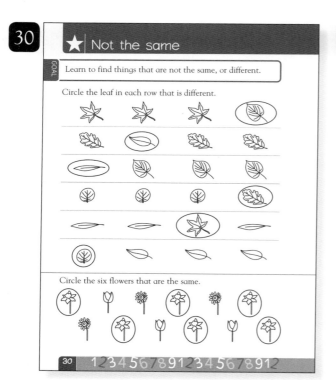

Circle the six flowers that are the same.

GOAL Learn to identify (spot) which is different.

Circle the animal in each row that is different.

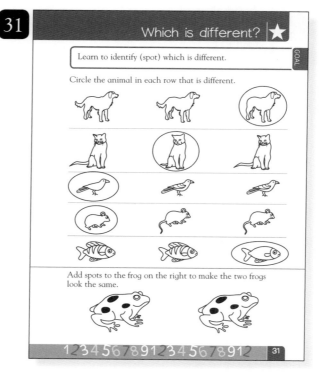

Add spots to the frog on the right to make the two frogs look the same.

Let children help with gardening or caring for houseplants. Reinforce classifying flowers and leaves that are the same and different. This helps build observation skills, which are important in learning math.

Read an illustrated book about animals with your child. Ask questions like, "What is different about those fish?" and "What is the same about these bears?" Describing what is different and what is the same helps children learn to compare things.

★ Which has more?

GOAL Count the objects to find out which set has more.

Write the letter **M** on the line under the box that has more objects.

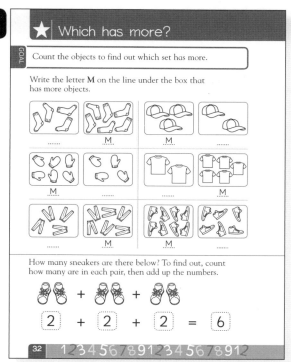

How many sneakers are there below? To find out, count how many are in each pair, then add up the numbers.

2 + 2 + 2 = 6

Encourage children to identify quantity by looking at objects without counting them. This introduces the skill of estimating. Display two jars of coins, one nearly full and one half full, and ask: "Which jar has more coins?"

Add one more ★

Learn to add one more.

Add one more to each group in the boxes. Then count the total items in the group and write the correct number.

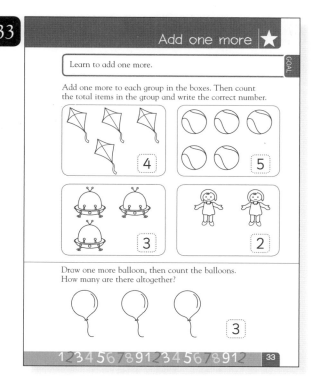

Draw one more balloon, then count the balloons. How many are there altogether?

3

Tell a simple story and draw simple pictures to reinforce adding. Here is an example: "Amy had two cookies. Adam gave her one more. How many cookies does Amy have now?"

★ Add more

GOAL Draw more shapes to add to the group. The + sign means to add.   ◯ + ◯◯ = 3

Draw two more of the same shape in each box. Then add all the shapes and write the correct number.

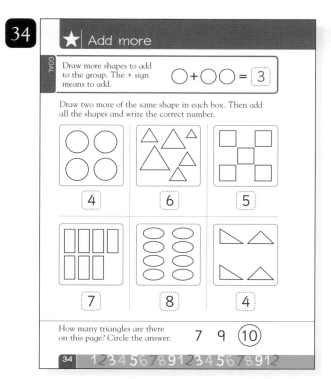

How many triangles are there on this page? Circle the answer.   7   9   (10)

Use the activities on this page to reinforce adding skills. Introduce the addition sign (+) by using it when helping children to write out the addition problems involved in adding more shapes to each box.

How many in total? ★

Find the total, which is the answer you get when you add things together.   ☁ + ☁ = 6

Draw a + sign between the boxes in each row. Then count all the items in both of the boxes and write the total number.

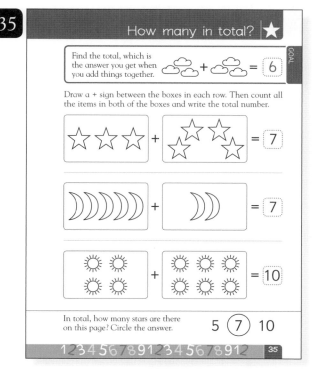

In total, how many stars are there on this page? Circle the answer.   5   (7)   10

Combining sets can be reinforced using objects such as plastic toys or buttons. Arrange objects in small groups according to shape or colour. Let children sort groups and gain an understanding of sorting and sets.

★ Which has fewer?

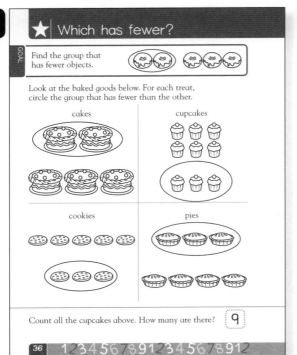

GOAL — Find the group that has fewer objects.

Look at the baked goods below. For each treat, circle the group that has fewer than the other.

cakes   cupcakes

cookies   pies

Count all the cupcakes above. How many are there? **9**

Guide children in looking for the group with fewer items. Model how to count the cakes in each group. Ask: "Which group has fewer cakes? Which group has more?"

Take away one ★

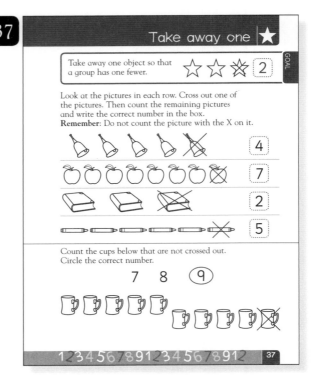

GOAL — Take away one object so that a group has one fewer. **2**

Look at the pictures in each row. Cross out one of the pictures. Then count the remaining pictures and write the correct number in the box.
Remember: Do not count the picture with the X on it.

4

7

2

5

Count the cups below that are not crossed out. Circle the correct number.

7   8   (9)

Introduce the concept of taking away, or subtracting, with a simple story. For example, "Tim had three toy cars. Tony took one car. How many cars did Tim have left?" Use toy cars to model the story.

★ Take away more

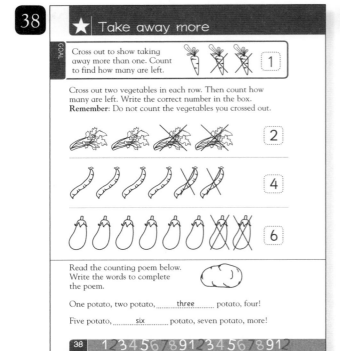

GOAL — Cross out to show taking away more than one. Count to find how many are left. **1**

Cross out two vegetables in each row. Then count how many are left. Write the correct number in the box.
Remember: Do not count the vegetables you crossed out.

2

4

6

Read the counting poem below. Write the words to complete the poem.

One potato, two potato, _____three_____ potato, four!

Five potato, _____six_____ potato, seven potato, more!

Children may need hands-on objects to be able to comprehend taking objects away and counting what's left. Use toys or plastic blocks to act out the activities on the page and to be sure children understand the basic idea of subtraction.

Subtract ★

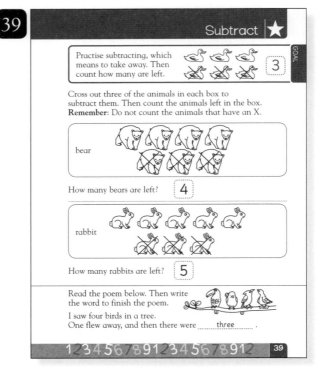

GOAL — Practise subtracting, which means to take away. Then count how many are left. **3**

Cross out three of the animals in each box to subtract them. Then count the animals left in the box.
Remember: Do not count the animals that have an X.

bear

How many bears are left? **4**

rabbit

How many rabbits are left? **5**

Read the poem below. Then write the word to finish the poem.
I saw four birds in a tree.
One flew away, and then there were _____three_____ .

Point to the sample problem to make sure children know what to do. Let them count the animals that remain after making an X on three animals. Then ask: "How many animals will be left if you take away three?"

★ Sorting objects into sets

GOAL | Add together groups to make sets of ten.

Draw a line from the group in the first column to the group in the second column that makes a set of ten.

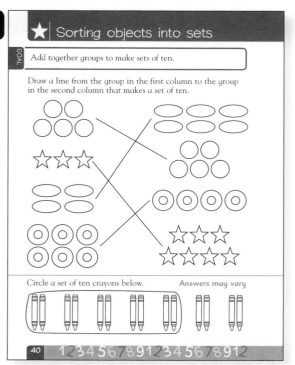

Circle a set of ten crayons below.   **Answers may vary**

Reinforce counting, sets, and shapes.
Cut cardboard into shapes, making sets
of ten of each shape. Place them in a
container. Engage children in taking them out of the
container one at a time and sorting them by
shape. Add a challenge by asking them to create
special sets, sets of five or two.

Which group? ★

GOAL | Learn to sort items into groups that are the same.

Draw a line to match the number on each child's shirt to the numbers on the flags below.

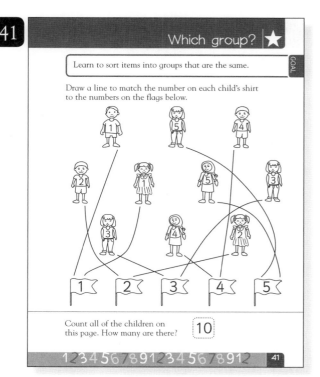

Count all of the children on this page. How many are there?   10

To extend the activity on the page, make a box
under each flag. Together, count the children
matched to each flag and write the correct
number in each box.

★ How many sets?

GOAL | Learn to match sets and find pairs.

Look at these socks. Find and match the correct pairs.

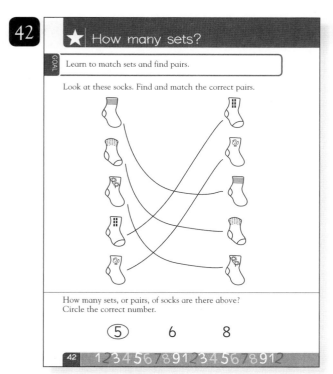

How many sets, or pairs, of socks are there above?
Circle the correct number.

⑤   6   8

Identifying sets helps children use the observation
skills they also need in reading, science, and
other areas of the curriculum. Finding and
matching sets also helps children begin to
develop problem-solving skills.

Counting sets ★

GOAL | Count to find the number of things in each set.

Count the farm animals in each box below. Then write the
correct number of animals next to each box.

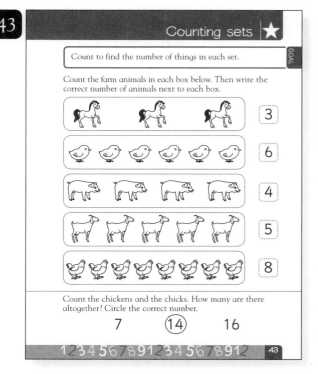

3

6

4

5

8

Count the chickens and the chicks. How many are there
altogether? Circle the correct number.

7   ⑭   16

Once children understand counting, challenge
them by asking questions that require them to
add two groups of objects. Use the activity on this
page for prompts. Ask: "How many pigs and goats
are there in all?"; "How many chicks and horses
are there altogether?"

★ Compare size

Compare the sizes of two objects to find the biggest.

Circle the biggest animal in each row below.

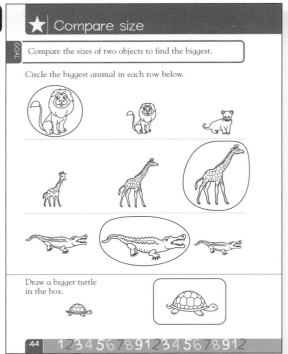

Draw a bigger turtle in the box.

Reinforce size and comparison by using pictures and key vocabulary words. Ask children questions to compare size: "Which animal in this row is the smallest?"; "Which animal in this row is bigger than the smallest one, and smaller than the biggest one?"

Draw bigger or smaller ★

Learn to draw objects that are bigger or smaller.

Look at each picture, and follow the directions.

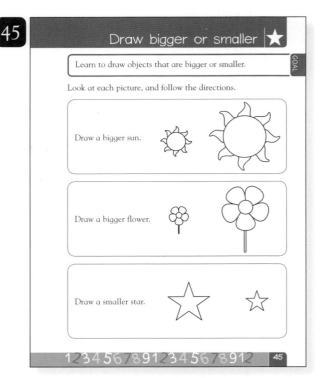

Draw a bigger sun.

Draw a bigger flower.

Draw a smaller star.

Encourage children to draw to help them learn to compare sizes. This requires little direction and lets children experiment as they develop independence in solving problems. They will also learn to use words related to size and shape.

★ Compare length

Compare the lengths of two objects to find which is shorter and which is longer.

Look at each row carefully. Follow the directions.

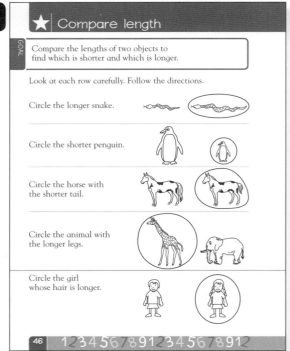

Circle the longer snake.

Circle the shorter penguin.

Circle the horse with the shorter tail.

Circle the animal with the longer legs.

Circle the girl whose hair is longer.

Ask questions about length while children are working with blocks or modelling clay. Make rows of blocks or roll out pieces of clay to different lengths. Ask: "Which is the longest?"; "Which is the shortest?"

Draw longer or shorter ★

Learn to draw objects that are longer or shorter.

Look at each picture. Follow the directions for each.

Longer

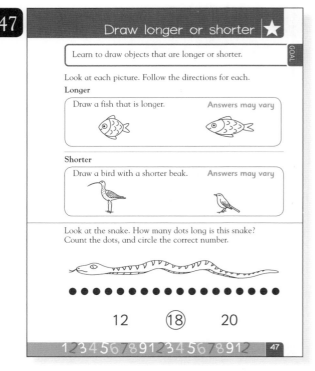

Draw a fish that is longer.   *Answers may vary*

Shorter

Draw a bird with a shorter beak.   *Answers may vary*

Look at the snake. How many dots long is this snake? Count the dots, and circle the correct number.

12   (18)   20

Show children how to estimate length. Display pieces of colourful yarn or strips of paper. Ask children to place them in order of length from the shortest to the longest.

★ Compare weight

Compare the weights of objects to find the heaviest.

Which weighs more? Circle the heavier object in each box.

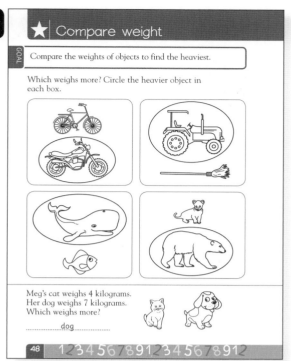

Meg's cat weighs 4 kilograms.
Her dog weighs 7 kilograms.
Which weighs more?

.... dog ....

Discuss with children different tools used to weigh things, such as the bathroom scale, the kitchen scale, and the scale at the supermarket. Let children use a small kitchen scale to weigh toys, dolls, or amounts of food.

Draw heavier or lighter ★

Learn to draw things that are heavier or lighter.

Look at the mouse below. In the empty box, draw an animal that is heavier than a mouse.

Look at the elephant below. In the empty box, draw an animal that is lighter than an elephant.

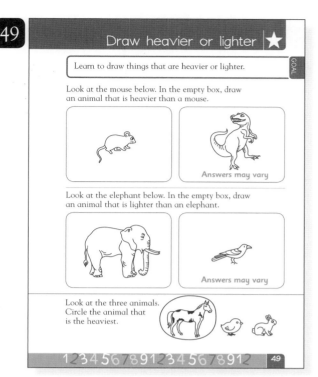

Answers may vary

Answers may vary

Look at the three animals.
Circle the animal that
is the heaviest.

Most children have prior knowledge about animals; though they may never have seen certain real animals, they have acquired knowledge from seeing animals in books and other places. Ask questions like, "How do you know that a horse is heavier than a chick?"

★ Position

Learn position words, which tell us where an object is placed.

Look at the picture below. Circle the words to answer each question.

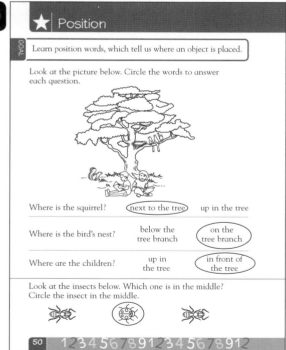

Where is the squirrel?	(next to the tree)	up in the tree
Where is the bird's nest?	below the tree branch	(on the tree branch)
Where are the children?	up in the tree	(in front of the tree)

Look at the insects below. Which one is in the middle?
Circle the insect in the middle.

Children may need help reading the questions and answers on this page. Read them aloud if necessary. Then solicit responses. It may be helpful to ask children to point to the picture and then respond with the correct position words.

More positions ★

Review position words:
inside   outside   above
          below   on   under

Look at the picture below. Circle the answer to each question.

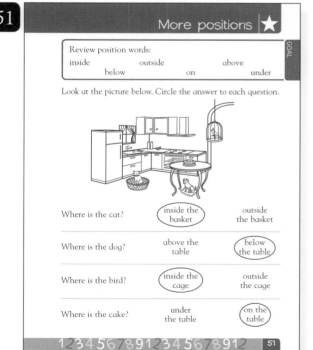

Where is the cat?	(inside the basket)	outside the basket
Where is the dog?	above the table	(below the table)
Where is the bird?	(inside the cage)	outside the cage
Where is the cake?	under the table	(on the table)

See if children can respond to the questions without reading the possible answers. Ask questions to encourage children to use the position words, and point to the correct answer, reading it aloud. This will help them make connections between pictures and words.

52

★ Telling the time

Learn to tell the time. A clock has two hands. The hour hand is short. The minute hand is long. The hour hand on this clock points to 3. The minute hand points to 12. That means the time is 3 o'clock.

3 o'clock

What time is shown on the clocks below?

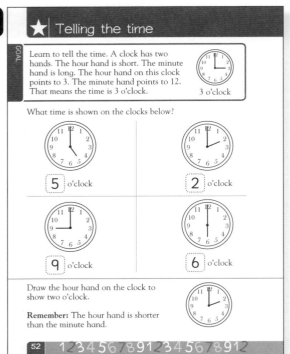

5 o'clock

2 o'clock

9 o'clock

6 o'clock

Draw the hour hand on the clock to show two o'clock.

Remember: The hour hand is shorter than the minute hand.

Incorporate time into daily conversations with children. Point to a clock, and say, "We have to get up at 7 o'clock tomorrow morning." Then ask, "Where will the hour hand be pointing at 7 o'clock?"

53

More clocks ★

Practise using clocks. When you write the word *o'clock*, that means the minute hand on the clock is pointing to 12. The hour hand points to the hour number.

Draw the hour hand on the clocks below to show the time that is under the clock.
Remember: The hour hand is shorter than the minute hand.

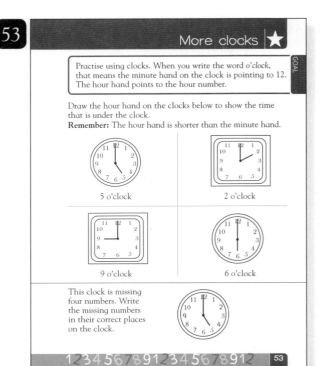

5 o'clock

2 o'clock

9 o'clock

6 o'clock

This clock is missing four numbers. Write the missing numbers in their correct places on the clock.

Tell children that the analogue clocks shown on this page, with hands that point to the time, are only one kind of clock. Explain that there are also digital clocks that are used on computers, cellphones, and alarm clocks. Digital clocks have no hands; they display numbers to tell you the time in hours and minutes.

54

★ Money

Learn the concept of using money to buy items.

Draw a line from each toy to the dollars that match the price of the toy.

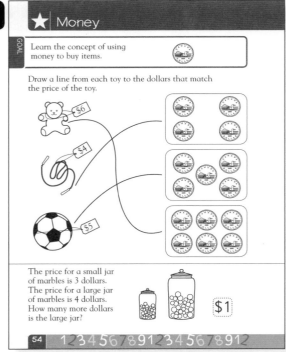

$6

$4

$5

The price for a small jar of marbles is 3 dollars. The price for a large jar of marbles is 4 dollars. How many more dollars is the large jar?

$1

As children match written dollar amounts with the quantity of loonies shown in the right-hand column, they will become familiar with counting and recognizing amounts of money. Let children act out buying toys with fake loonies you create together, or fake paper dollars from a board game.

55

Count the money ★

Count coins to find the total amount of money.

Count the money in each pocket. Draw a line from each pocket to the correct amount written in the middle column.

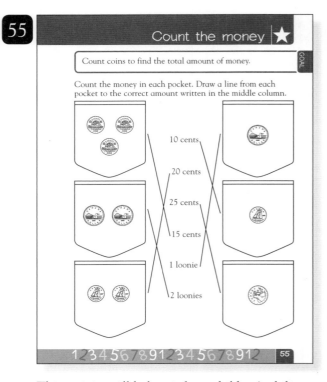

10 cents

20 cents

25 cents

15 cents

1 loonie

2 loonies

This activity will help reinforce children's ability to count money and recognize the value of coins. Having coins on hand may be helpful. Let children count real coins to match the quantities listed on the page.

58

★ Garden

A garden is a small piece of land where flowers, fruits, and vegetables are grown. Some animals live in a garden, too.

Can you find the animals living in the garden? Point to each animal and name it. Describe animals that live in a garden near you.

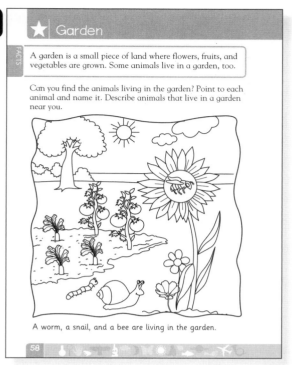

A worm, a snail, and a bee are living in the garden.

What other creatures besides those pictured might live in a garden? Explore your own yard or park with your child and discover the plants and animals that live there. Have them identify similarities and differences between local environments.

59

Plants ★

A plant has many parts to help it grow.

Find each part of the plant and say its name.

This plant is a tulip.

The flower is where the seeds are made so that new plants can grow.

The stem of the tulip brings water to all the parts of the plant.

The leaves take in sunlight for the plant so it can make food.

The roots of the tulip grow in the ground and help the plant get water.

Some parts of a plant have reproductive functions, others take in water, while others convert sunlight into energy or attract insects to help with pollination. Talk about the role each part plays in keeping the plant healthy.

60

★ Trees

A tree is a large plant. The stem of a tree is made out of wood.

Touch each part of the tree and say its name.

This tree has many of the same parts as the tulip plant you saw on page 59.

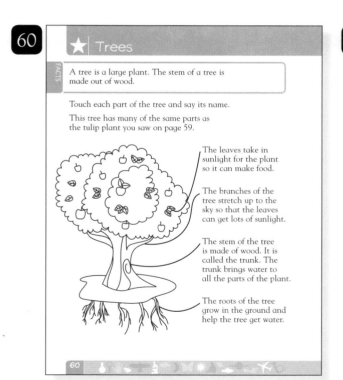

The leaves take in sunlight for the plant so it can make food.

The branches of the tree stretch up to the sky so that the leaves can get lots of sunlight.

The stem of the tree is made of wood. It is called the trunk. The trunk brings water to all the parts of the plant.

The roots of the tree grow in the ground and help the tree get water.

Plants may look very different, but they all have the same parts that perform the same functions. Ask your child to compare the parts of the tulip to the parts of the tree. How are they alike? How are they different?

61

Falling leaves ★

Some trees lose their leaves in the fall and grow new leaves in the spring.

During the summer, trees have all their leaves. During the fall, the leaves of some trees fall to the ground. During the winter, you only see the branches of these trees. During the spring, the leaves grow back. Point to each tree and name the season it is in.

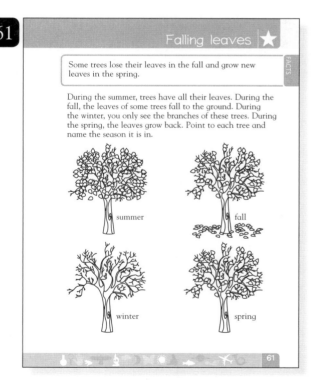

summer

fall

winter

spring

Children of this age will be familiar with the seasonal changes. Discuss how the leaves and trees change with each season and how these and other changes repeat themselves. These patterns of change are called cycles and are part of our environment.

★ Plants we eat

Many foods that we eat are plants.

Point to the two plants that we eat, and name them.

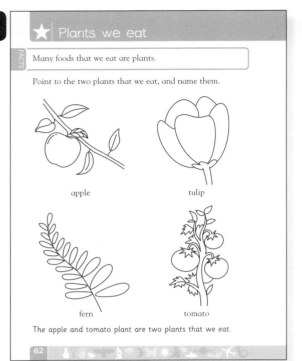

apple

tulip

fern

tomato

The apple and tomato plant are two plants that we eat.

The concept of turning plants into food (i.e., turning tomatoes into tomato sauce) is a difficult one for this age group. A hands-on activity such as cooking can make the concept easier to grasp.

Vegetables ★

Vegetables come from different parts of plants.

The roots of a plant grow in the ground and help the plant get water. Carrots and potatoes are root vegetables. The stem of the plant brings water to all the parts of the plant. Asparagus and celery are stems. The leaves take in sunlight for the plant so it can make food. Spinach and lettuce are leaf vegetables.

Point to each vegetable below, and say its name. Is it a root, stem, or leaf vegetable?

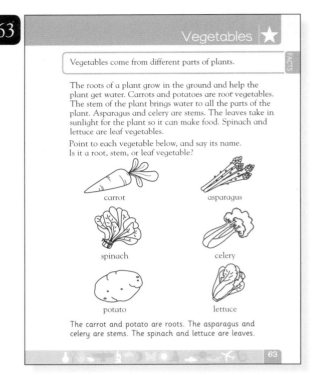

carrot

asparagus

spinach

celery

potato

lettuce

The carrot and potato are roots. The asparagus and celery are stems. The spinach and lettuce are leaves.

Your child will have learned about the different parts of plants and how we use plants for food. This exercise helps to reinforce both of these lessons.

★ Fruits

A fruit is the part of a plant that contains seeds.

Circle the fruit in each picture.

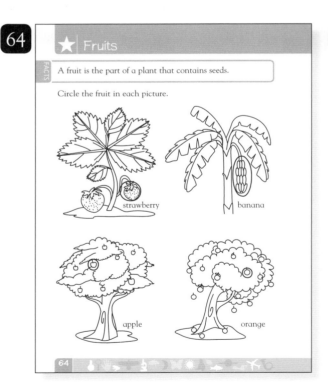

strawberry

banana

apple

orange

All fruits contain seeds, but not all fruits and seeds are easy to identify. Show your child fruits that might not be readily recognized, such as pumpkins and cucumbers, and explain that it is the seeds that make these plants fruit.

Useful plants ★

Many things we use are made from plants and trees.

Connect each plant with the things that are made from it.

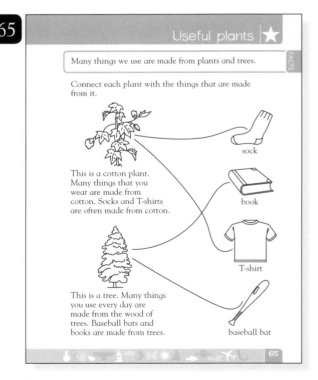

sock

This is a cotton plant. Many things that you wear are made from cotton. Socks and T-shirts are often made from cotton.

book

T-shirt

This is a tree. Many things you use every day are made from the wood of trees. Baseball bats and books are made from trees.

baseball bat

Understanding the concept that many items can be made from trees and plants can be tricky for children. Look for other things around the home that are made from plants and discuss these.

★ Plants and water

FACTS

Plants need water to grow.

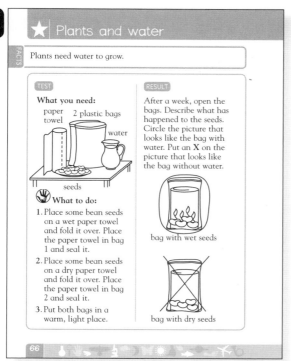

TEST

What you need:
paper towel   2 plastic bags
water
seeds

What to do:
1. Place some bean seeds on a wet paper towel and fold it over. Place the paper towel in bag 1 and seal it.
2. Place some bean seeds on a dry paper towel and fold it over. Place the paper towel in bag 2 and seal it.
3. Put both bags in a warm, light place.

RESULT

After a week, open the bags. Describe what has happened to the seeds. Circle the picture that looks like the bag with water. Put an **X** on the picture that looks like the bag without water.

bag with wet seeds

bag with dry seeds

Experimentation involves observing, questioning, and sharing. The point of these activities for children is to observe what happens when a plant receives light and water and what happens when it doesn't. Ask the child to predict what

Plants and light ★

FACTS

Plants need light to grow.

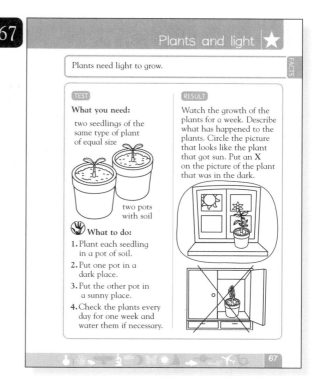

TEST

What you need:
two seedlings of the same type of plant of equal size

two pots with soil

What to do:
1. Plant each seedling in a pot of soil.
2. Put one pot in a dark place.
3. Put the other pot in a sunny place.
4. Check the plants every day for one week and water them if necessary.

RESULT

Watch the growth of the plants for a week. Describe what has happened to the plants. Circle the picture that looks like the plant that got sun. Put an **X** on the picture of the plant that was in the dark.

will happen to each plant. Making predictions is an important part of experimentation. Comparing results to predictions and discussing the experiment's outcome are also key activities.

★ Seeds

FACTS

Seeds need to travel to different places to grow new plants. They travel to find a place that has light and water.

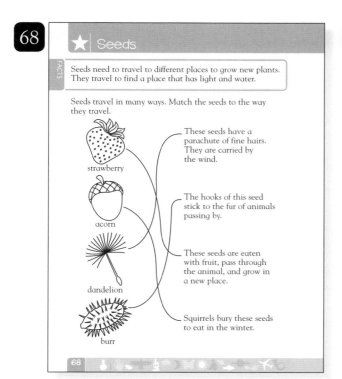

Seeds travel in many ways. Match the seeds to the way they travel.

strawberry

acorn

dandelion

burr

These seeds have a parachute of fine hairs. They are carried by the wind.

The hooks of this seed stick to the fur of animals passing by.

These seeds are eaten with fruit, pass through the animal, and grow in a new place.

Squirrels bury these seeds to eat in the winter.

Naming and recognizing the different ways that seeds travel is an excellent way to explain how seeds move to different locations. See if your child can name other seeds that travel in the same way as those listed.

My habitat ★

FACTS

A habitat is a place where an animal or plant naturally lives or grows.

Draw a picture of of your home. Draw and name animals and plants that live and grow in and around your home. Make sure you include you and your family.

Drawings may vary

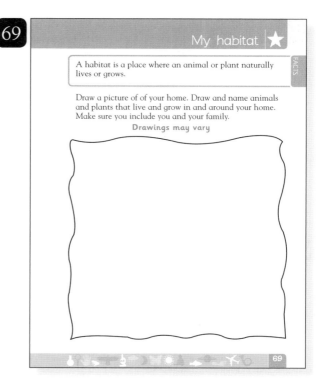

Children at this age are drawn to what is familiar, and they will understand habitats that are closer to where they live, such as lakes, gardens, and forests. Rainforests, mountains, and deserts are abstract concepts and are more difficult for children at this age to understand. They will learn about these habitats in older grades

★ Ocean

An ocean is a large body of water. Ocean water is salty. Many animals live in the ocean.

Draw a picture of an animal that lives in the ocean. Then colour the picture.
Answers may vary

The ocean may be too abstract for your child to understand if he or she has not travelled to one before. Browse through various books about oceans at a bookstore, library, or online. Explain that most of the world's water is contained in oceans. Look at photos of animals that live in the ocean.

Pond ★

A pond is a small body of fresh water.

Colour the animals and plants in this picture of a pond. Can you name all the animals?

The animals in the picture are a duck and ducklings, a beaver, a dragonfly, fish, a frog, and a turtle.

If you can, take a field trip with your child to a pond. Take note of all the plants and animals you can see. Discuss with your child how the different animals depend on the pond for their survival.

★ Eating habits

Some animals eat only plants. Some animals eat only other animals.

Circle all of the animals that eat only plants. Point to the animals that eat only other animals and say their names out loud.

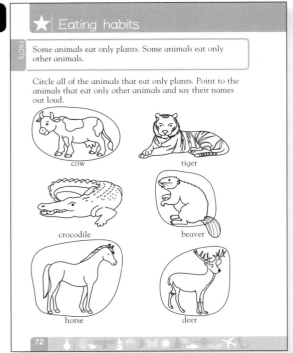

cow   tiger

crocodile   beaver

horse   deer

The terms "carnivores" (animals that eat only other animals) and "herbivores" (animals that only eat plants) are too advanced for your child at this age. Children will learn these concepts in a later grade.

What I like to eat ★

Some animals eat both plants and animals.

Human beings eat both plants and animals. What do you like to eat? Draw your favourite food that comes from a plant in the **Plants** box. Draw your favourite food that comes from an animal in the **Animals** box.
Answers may vary

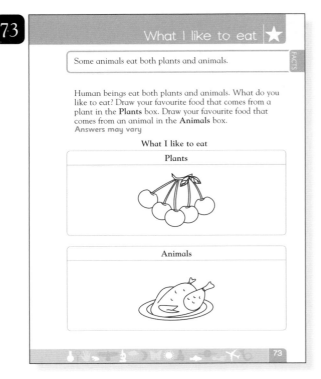

What I like to eat

Plants

Animals

Discuss which foods your child eats come from plants and which foods come from animals. Some foods, such as cheese and milk, may be harder for children to identify, so you may need to prompt them.

★ Sight

We see with our eyes.

Colour the eyes the same as yours. Then write your name beside the picture.

Answers may vary

Draw the missing eyes on these animals.

We use our sense of sight to observe our surroundings. Playing a game such as "I Spy" helps children understand how they can see, observe, and describe the world around them.

Hot and cold ★

Hot and cold describe the temperature of something. Something that is hot has a high temperature. Something that is cold has a low temperature. A thermometer is used to measure how hot or cold something is.

Point to the pictures of the things that are hot. Circle the pictures of the things that are cold.

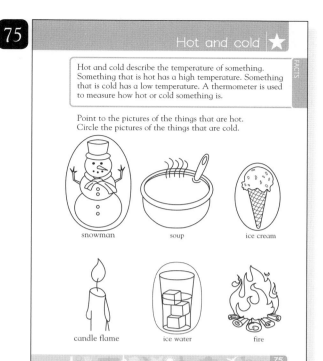

snowman   soup   ice cream

candle flame   ice water   fire

Hot and cold can be difficult concepts to describe to children of this age. Using a thermometer to test the temperature of different items to show how hot or cold something is can make this concept easier for children to grasp.

★ Hearing

We hear with our ears.

Circle the things you can hear with your ears.

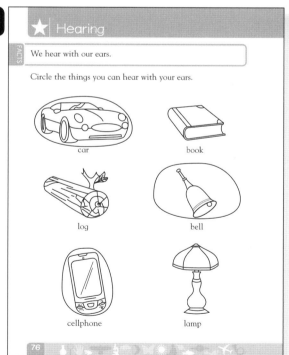

car   book

log   bell

cellphone   lamp

In this activity your child identified the sounds of objects that make noise. Have them name animals that make sounds and imitate the sound each animal makes.

Volume ★

A noise can be loud or quiet. If you are close to a noise, it sounds loud. If you are far away from a noise, it sounds quiet.

The dog is barking. Which child hears the dog's bark the loudest? Colour that child's shirt red. Which child hears the dog's bark the quietest? Colour that child's shirt blue. Then colour the whole picture.

Some sounds are loud and some are quiet. Play a game with your child in which you each name things that make a loud noise and things that make a quiet noise.

★ Touch

We use our fingers to feel things. Our fingers tell us if things are hard, soft, rough, smooth, hot, or cold.

TEST **What you need:**

Gather up a variety of objects from around your house. The objects shown below will work well for this activity, but you can choose others if you like.

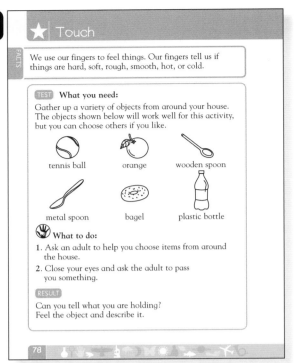

tennis ball   orange   wooden spoon

metal spoon   bagel   plastic bottle

What to do:

1. Ask an adult to help you choose items from around the house.
2. Close your eyes and ask the adult to pass you something.

RESULT

Can you tell what you are holding?
Feel the object and describe it.

Continue to support your child in this activity by having them not only identify items, but also describe how each object feels. Is it heavy? Smooth? Squishy? Encourage them to use their adjectives.

Smell ★

We use our nose to smell things.

Circle the things you can smell with your nose.

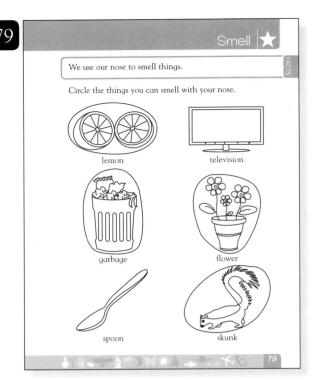

lemon   television

garbage   flower

spoon   skunk

Continue to support your child with this activity by coming up with other things that have a strong smell. What things smell sweet? What things are stinky? Think of different descriptive adjectives.

★ Smell test

The nose can detect many different smells.

TEST

What you need:

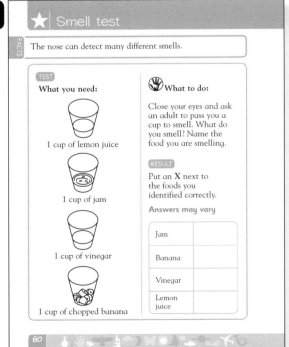

1 cup of lemon juice

1 cup of jam

1 cup of vinegar

1 cup of chopped banana

What to do:

Close your eyes and ask an adult to pass you a cup to smell. What do you smell? Name the food you are smelling.

RESULT

Put an **X** next to the foods you identified correctly.

Answers may vary

Jam	
Banana	
Vinegar	
Lemon juice	

This science activity is a great way for children to experience how their sense of smell helps them collect information and make scientific observations.

Taste ★

We taste food with our tongues.

Foods can taste sweet, salty, or sour. What do these foods taste like? Connect each food to its taste.

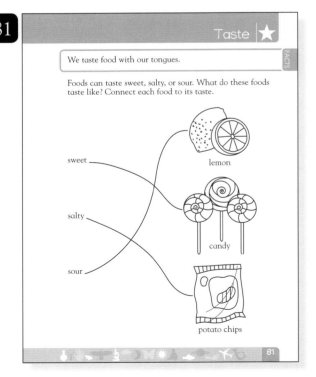

sweet

salty

sour

lemon

candy

potato chips

Encourage your child to name other foods that are sweet, salty, and sour. Which taste do they like the best? Which taste do they like the least?

★ Animals

Animals come in many shapes and sizes.

Animals move in different ways. Some animals walk and run. Some animals swim. Some animals fly. Animals that fly have wings. Circle each animal that has wings.

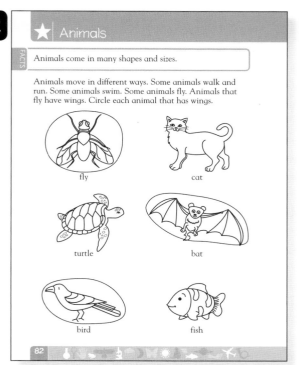

fly — cat — turtle — bat — bird — fish

Continue learning about how animals get around and move. Name animals that swim. Name animals that walk and run. How do humans move around?

Tame and wild animals ★

Some animals are wild. Other animals can be kept in a house. These animals are tame.

Circle the animals that are wild. Point to the animals that are tame and can be kept in a house.

dog — gorilla — fox — goldfish — hamster — lion

Children often know the difference between tame and wild animals at this point. Encourage them to name more wild animals and where these animals live. Also, talk about how wild animals behave differently than tame animals.

★ Pets

Tame animals can live in your home and be kept as pets.

Do you have a pet?

If you have a pet, what kind of animal is your pet?

What is your pet's name?

Do you have a friend who has a pet?

If you have a friend who has a pet, what kind of animal is that pet?

What is the name of your friend's pet?

Draw your favourite pet.   **Answers may vary**

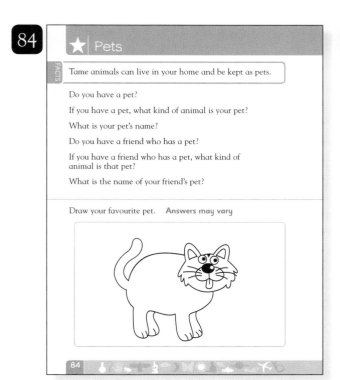

Tame animals live in captivity. Discuss with your child the different homes where tame animals might live: for instance, in a home, in a cage, in a corral.

Pet care ★

Pets need special care to keep them happy and healthy.

The pictures below show some of the things pets need to be happy and healthy. Point to the pictures of the things pets need and name them all. Can you think of anything else pets need?

food and water	exercise
home	medical care

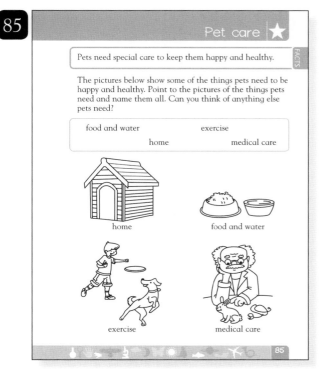

home — food and water — exercise — medical care

Unlike wild animals, which provide their own food and shelter, tame animals rely on humans to take care of them. What other needs do tame animals have? Many of their needs are the same as humans'. Feel free to talk about farm animals as well as pets.

86

★ Motion

FACTS

Motion is how things move.

The words in the box describe some of the ways things move. Say the words aloud and point to the picture of the motion each word describes.

| spin | slide | fall | fly | bounce | roll |

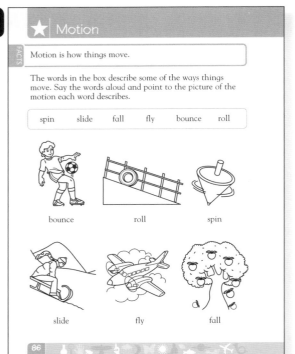

bounce   roll   spin

slide   fly   fall

In addition to the examples given in the exercise, ask your child to name other things that move in the same ways. For example: What else can fly? What other objects roll? Can children spin? Collect items from around the house to demonstrate each action.

87

Pushing and pulling ★

FACTS

When you move something away from you, you push it. When you move something closer to you, you pull it.

Look at each picture. Put an X in the box to say if the movement shows pushing or pulling.

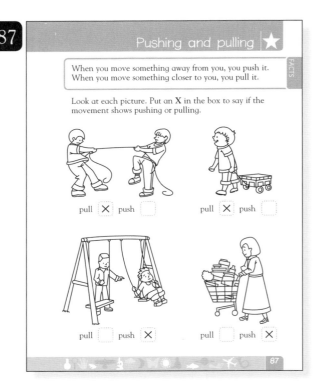

pull [X] push [ ]   pull [X] push [ ]

pull [ ] push [X]   pull [ ] push [X]

An object won't move unless something pushes or pulls on it (a force). A moving object will keep going in a straight line unless something pushes or pulls on it. Have your child push around a ball to demonstrate this concept in a concrete way.

88

★ Light

FACTS

Light helps us to see.

Circle the things that generate light.

tree   campfire

flashlight   sun

book   lamp

Your child understands that we need light to see. Brainstorm with them and see how many other light sources you can come up with. For example, the moon, the stars, light bulbs, fireflies, matches, fireworks, and lasers. Draw these on a poster.

Make shadow puppets ★

FACTS

A shadow is a dark patch that forms where an object blocks out light.

TEST

What you need:

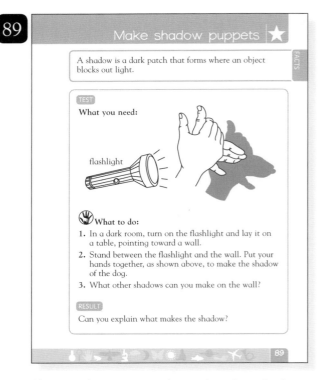

flashlight

What to do:

1. In a dark room, turn on the flashlight and lay it on a table, pointing toward a wall.
2. Stand between the flashlight and the wall. Put your hands together, as shown above, to make the shadow of the dog.
3. What other shadows can you make on the wall?

RESULT

Can you explain what makes the shadow?

Play outside on a sunny day to show how shadows are made in the sun. Measure your child's shadows at different times of the day—morning, noon, and late afternoon—and discuss how his/her shadow changes. Have your child stand outside on a sunny day and use sidewalk chalk to draw around the shadow they make.

★ A rainbow

A rainbow is an arch of colours that appears when the sun shines through rain.

Colour the rainbow.

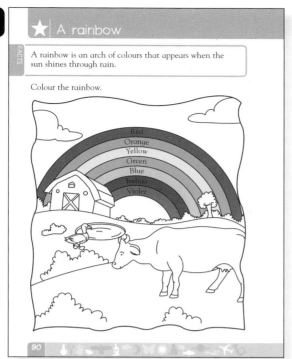

Red
Orange
Yellow
Green
Blue
Indigo
Violet

Try another tactile exercise to illustrate the colours of a rainbow. Use coloured candies or coloured cereal to create a 3-D rainbow. Glue the candies or cereal to a sheet of blue construction paper

Make a rainbow ★

You can make a rainbow by shining a light through water.

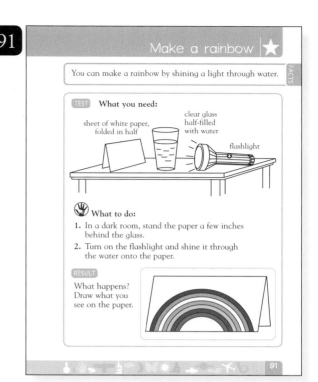

TEST What you need:

sheet of white paper, folded in half

clear glass half-filled with water

flashlight

What to do:

1. In a dark room, stand the paper a few inches behind the glass.
2. Turn on the flashlight and shine it through the water onto the paper.

RESULT

What happens? Draw what you see on the paper.

and have your child say the colours aloud. Here's a trick for remembering the rainbow colour order: Roy. G. Biv.

★ Solids, liquids, and gases

The things around you are solids, liquids, or gases.

Solid things keep their shape. Liquid things take the shape of the container they are in. Gases get bigger to fill the space they are in. Circle all the liquids. Point to the solids.

books

candy

juice

balloons

milk

water

Books and candy are solids.

Children this age find it difficult to understand the abstract properties of matter. They will, however, be able to group materials into states like solids and liquids.

Gas ★

Air is a gas. Air is invisible but you can feel it and see that it is there by blowing bubbles.

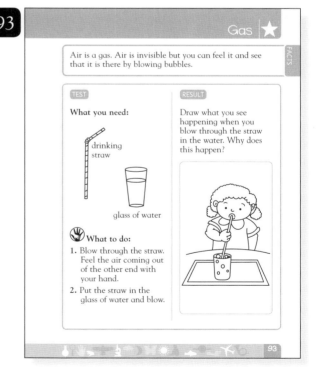

TEST

What you need:

drinking straw

glass of water

What to do:

1. Blow through the straw. Feel the air coming out of the other end with your hand.
2. Put the straw in the glass of water and blow.

RESULT

Draw what you see happening when you blow through the straw in the water. Why does this happen?

Hands-on experiments help them identify different forms of matter. Concentrate on shapes and teach them to differentiate forms of matter based on shape. Reinforce the concepts they have already learned.

94

★ Balloons

You can fill a balloon with air.

TEST

What you need:

balloon

✋ **What to do:**

1. Ask an adult to blow into a balloon and fill it with air.
2. Take the balloon in your fingers and hold the mouth firmly to keep the air in.
3. Stretch the mouth of the balloon. Can you hear the air make a squeaky noise as it escapes?
4. Now let go of the balloon.

RESULT

Describe what happened to the balloon. Why do you think this happened?

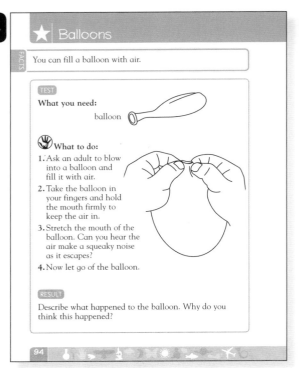

This exercise illustrates that gases such as air will fill the space that they are in. They also learn that gases are present but often invisible. The concept of gas is a more difficult concept for your child to understand at this level.

95

Wind ★

Wind is moving air.

Draw a circle around the things that use the wind. Colour the picture. **Colours may vary**

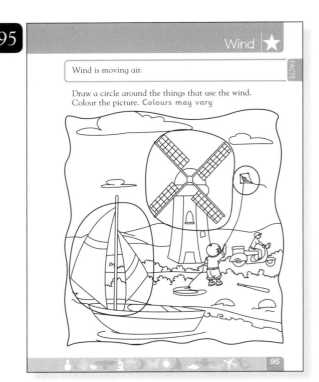

Here, the child learns that wind is moving air and that wind has force, as it did when it moved the balloon across the room in the previous exercise. These are not necessarily easy concepts for children of this age, so you may need to discuss.

96

★ Liquid

Liquid takes the shape of the container it is in.

TEST

What you need:

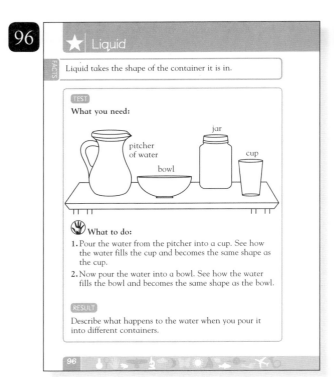

jar

pitcher of water

bowl

cup

✋ **What to do:**

1. Pour the water from the pitcher into a cup. See how the water fills the cup and becomes the same shape as the cup.
2. Now pour the water into a bowl. See how the water fills the bowl and becomes the same shape as the bowl.

RESULT

Describe what happens to the water when you pour it into different containers.

As they experiment with the water, your child will learn in a concrete way that liquids take the shapes of their containers. They will also discover that liquids are visible and can be seen.

97

Bubbles ★

Bubbles are liquid filled with air.

TEST

What you need:

2 tablespoons of dish soap

water

pipe cleaner

RESULT

Draw what happens.

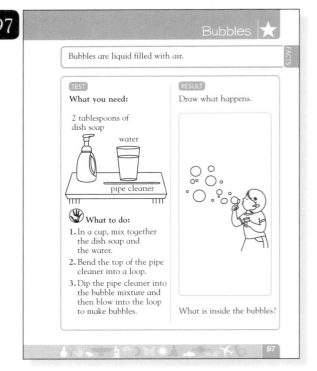

✋ **What to do:**

1. In a cup, mix together the dish soap and the water.
2. Bend the top of the pipe cleaner into a loop.
3. Dip the pipe cleaner into the bubble mixture and then blow into the loop to make bubbles.

What is inside the bubbles?

Reinforcing scientific concepts with play makes learning fun for children. This activity demonstrates that bubbles are a liquid filled with air, and it's the air that makes them float.

Solids keep their shape.

Draw a line between each object and the shape it matches.

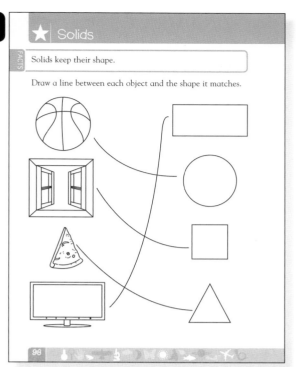

In addition to demonstrating how solids keep their form, this exercise shows how drawing lines to match up the objects to their shapes help kids practise their shapes. Line drawing also helps develop fine motor skills.

Water can be liquid or solid.

TEST

What you need: water pitcher
bowl   ice-cube tray

What to do:
1. Pour water into a pitcher. Is this water solid or liquid?
2. Pour the water from the pitcher into an ice-cube tray.
3. Put the ice-cube tray in the freezer for 5 hours.
4. Take the ice-cube tray out of the freezer and put the ice cubes in a bowl. Is the ice solid or liquid?
5. Keep the bowl of ice on a counter overnight. Look at the bowl in the morning.

RESULT

What happened to the water in the freezer?
What happened to the ice in the bowl?

What makes the water change between a solid and a liquid?

Here, your child sees that water can change from one state to another. For an added element to the experiment, leave the water out long enough for it to evaporate and become a gas. Discuss the results.

Freezing is when a liquid changes into a solid.
Freezing happens when it is very cold.

Look at the pictures. Circle the thing that will freeze in the cold.

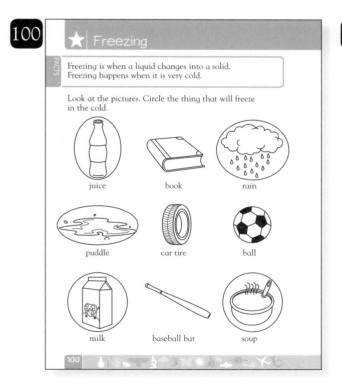

juice   book   rain
puddle   car tire   ball
milk   baseball bat   soup

This activity illustrates how matter can change shape by freezing and melting and how temperature is vital in this change.

Melting is when a solid turns into a liquid.
Melting happens when it is very warm.

Draw a circle around the objects that melt when it is hot.

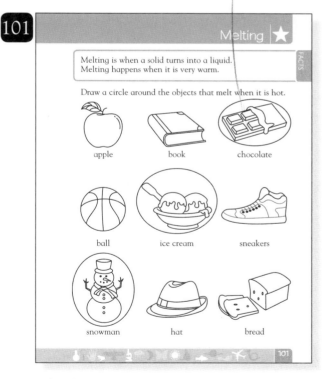

apple   book   chocolate
ball   ice cream   sneakers
snowman   hat   bread

When liquids are cooled enough they freeze. When solids are heated enough they become liquid.

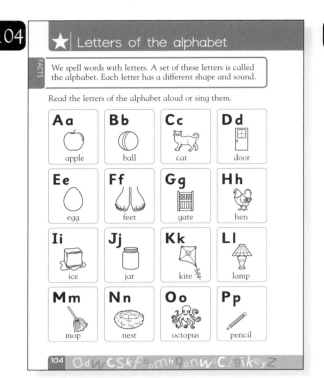

104

★ Letters of the alphabet

We spell words with letters. A set of these letters is called the alphabet. Each letter has a different shape and sound.

Read the letters of the alphabet aloud or sing them.

A a apple	**B b** ball	**C c** cat	**D d** door
E e egg	**F f** feet	**G g** gate	**H h** hen
I i ice	**J j** jar	**K k** kite	**L l** lamp
M m mop	**N n** nest	**O o** octopus	**P p** pencil

You can make a set of reusable cards from pages 104 and 105. Photocopy the pages, laminate them, and then cut out the individual letter cards. You can glue cord onto the letters before laminating them so that your child can touch and feel each letter.

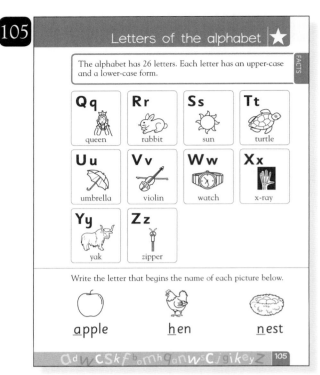

105

Letters of the alphabet ★

The alphabet has 26 letters. Each letter has an upper-case and a lower-case form.

Q q queen	**R r** rabbit	**S s** sun	**T t** turtle
U u umbrella	**V v** violin	**W w** watch	**X x** x-ray
Y y yak	**Z z** zipper		

Write the letter that begins the name of each picture below.

apple   hen   nest

Review each letter with your child and work together to come up with places where he or she has seen the letter—perhaps in a name, on a sign, or in his or her city, town, or street address.

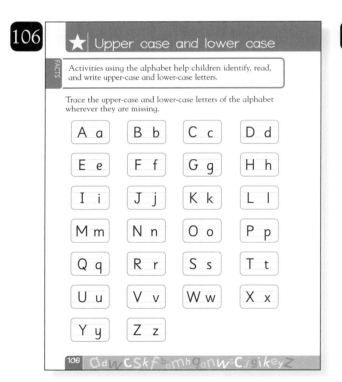

106

★ Upper case and lower case

Activities using the alphabet help children identify, read, and write upper-case and lower-case letters.

Trace the upper-case and lower-case letters of the alphabet wherever they are missing.

A a	B b	C c	D d
E e	F f	G g	H h
I i	J j	K k	L l
M m	N n	O o	P p
Q q	R r	S s	T t
U u	V v	W w	X x
Y y	Z z		

This activity gives your child practice in writing upper-case and lower-case letters and forming them correctly. Ask your child to say the name of each letter aloud as he or she traces it.

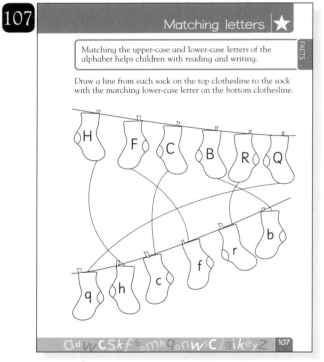

107

Matching letters ★

Matching the upper-case and lower-case letters of the alphabet helps children with reading and writing.

Draw a line from each sock on the top clothesline to the sock with the matching lower-case letter on the bottom clothesline.

This activity will help your child have a better understanding of corresponding upper-case and lower-case letters. Use pages 104 and 105, or the cards you made, to review other corresponding upper-case and lower-case letters.

★ Vowels and consonants

FACTS Words are spelled with letters. Some letters are consonants and some are vowels. The letters **a, e, i, o,** and **u** are vowels. The letter **y** is sometimes a vowel and sometimes a consonant. The other letters of the alphabet are consonants.

Read each picture's name aloud. Circle the vowel you hear in the middle of each word.

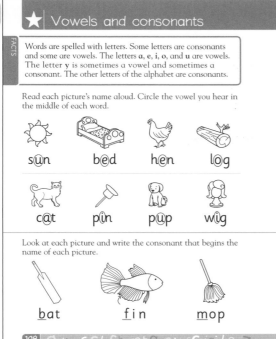

s(u)n   b(e)d   h(e)n   l(o)g

c(a)t   p(i)n   p(u)p   w(i)g

Look at each picture and write the consonant that begins the name of each picture.

bat   **f**in   **m**op

Teach your child to distinguish vowels from consonants. Let him or her sort letter blocks or cards into vowels and consonants while saying each letter. Say some simple words and ask your child to identify the middle vowel. For example, "What's the middle letter in the word 'hat'?"

Letter sounds ★

FACTS Each letter has a different sound. For example, the letters **b-a-t** spell "bat." The letters **b-u-g** spell "bug."

Look at each picture and say its name aloud. Then write the letters of its name in the boxes in the correct order.

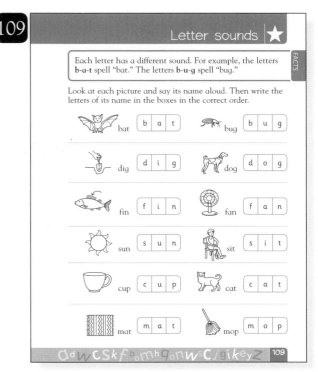

bat | b | a | t | bug | b | u | g |

dig | d | i | g | dog | d | o | g |

fin | f | i | n | fan | f | a | n |

sun | s | u | n | sit | s | i | t |

cup | c | u | p | cat | c | a | t |

mat | m | a | t | mop | m | o | p |

Help your child connect sounds to printed text. This provides a way for your child to approach new words. Help him or her say the sound of each letter in the words above. Practise this often when you talk about new words.

★ Consonants b, c, d, and f

FACTS The letter **b** begins the word "book." The letter **c** begins the word "cat." The letter **d** begins the word "duck." The letter **f** begins the word "fun."

Trace the upper-case and lower-case letters in each row. Circle the picture in each row whose name begins with the same letter.

Bb Bb Bb   leaf   bell

Cc Cc Cc   cup   pot

Dd Dd Dd   hen   dog

Ff Ff Ff   fan   net

Find pictures of things that begin with **b, c, d,** and **f**. Label small boxes with the letters. Play a sorting game. Let your child say the name of each picture and then place it in the correct box.

Consonants g, h, j, and k ★

FACTS The letter **g** begins the word "gift." The letter **h** begins the word "hut." The letter **j** begins the word "jump." The letter **k** begins the word "kite."

Trace the upper-case and lower-case letters in each row. Circle the picture in each row whose name begins with the same letter.

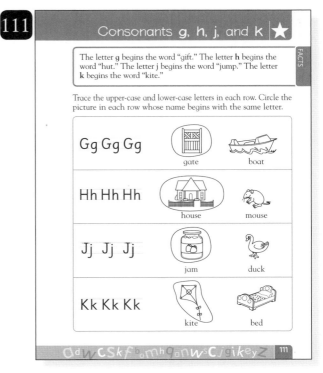

Gg Gg Gg   gate   boat

Hh Hh Hh   house   mouse

Jj Jj Jj   jam   duck

Kk Kk Kk   kite   bed

Ask your child to think of five words that begin with **g**, five words that begin with **h**, five that begin with **j**, and five that begin with **k**. Offer help if your child needs it. You could also add that **g** sometimes has a **j** sound, as in the word "gentle."

112

⭐ Consonants l, m, n, and p

FACTS

The letter **l** begins the word "lamp." The letter **m** begins the word "mop." The letter **n** begins the word "net." The letter **p** begins the word "pan."

Trace the upper-case and lower-case letters at the beginning of each row. Circle the two words in each row that begin with the same letter.

Ll Ll Ll — (leaf) (log) candle

MmMmMm — (mug) boot (moon)

Nn Nn Nn — (nurse) (nest) swing

Pp Pp Pp — (puppy) bat (pencil)

Play the sorting game again. Find pictures of things that begin with **l**, **m**, **n**, and **p**. Label small boxes with the letters. Let your child say the name of each picture and then place it in the correct box.

113

Consonants q, r, s, and t ⭐

FACTS

The letter **q** begins the word "quilt." The letter **r** begins the word "rabbit." The letter **s** begins the word "sock." The letter **t** begins the word "top."

Trace the upper-case and lower-case letters at the beginning of each row. Circle the two words in each row that begin with the same letter.

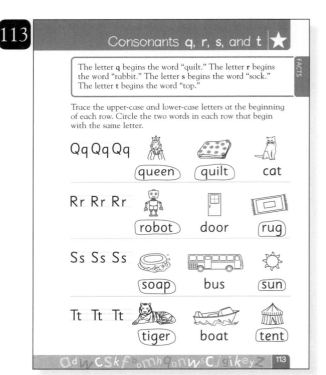

Qq Qq Qq — (queen) (quilt) cat

Rr Rr Rr — (robot) door (rug)

Ss Ss Ss — (soap) bus (sun)

Tt Tt Tt — (tiger) boat (tent)

Reinforce how to pronounce the letters **q**, **r**, **s**, and **t**. Say words beginning with these letters and let your child repeat each word aloud. Words could include "quarter," "round," "super," and "tongue."

114

⭐ Consonants v, w, x, y, and z

FACTS

The letter **v** begins the word "van." The letter **w** begins the word "window." The letter **x** begins the word "x-ray." The letter **y** begins the word "yard." The letter **z** begins the word "zebra."

Trace the upper-case and lower-case letters at the beginning of each row. Circle the word or words in each row that begin with the same letter.

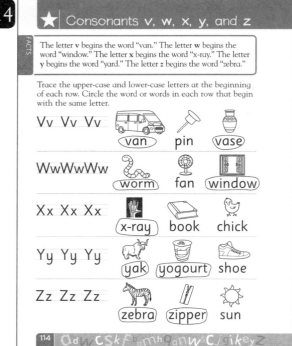

Vv Vv Vv — (van) pin (vase)

WwWwWw — (worm) fan (window)

Xx Xx Xx — (x-ray) book chick

Yy Yy Yy — (yak) (yogourt) shoe

Zz Zz Zz — (zebra) (zipper) sun

Ask your child to think of more words that begin with or contain these less commonly used consonants. Examples include "voice," "watch," "fox," "you," and "pizza." Don't forget to remind your child that the letter **y** is sometimes used as a vowel, too.

Letter sounds ⭐

FACTS

Words have different sounds based on the order of the letters they contain. If the beginning, middle, or final letters of a word change, a new word with a different sound is made.

Read each pair of words below. Then underline the letters that are different in each pair.

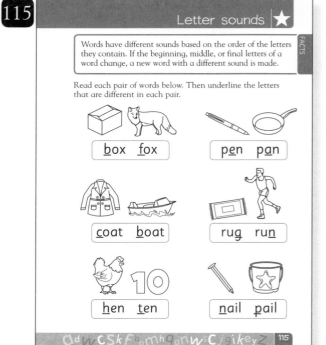

box fox

pen pan

coat boat

rug run

hen ten

nail pail

Practise sounding out the initial and other sounds of words. Make sure your child understands the terms beginning, or initial, middle, and ending sounds. Use the word "hen," for example, and exaggerate the sound of each letter.

★ Beginning sounds

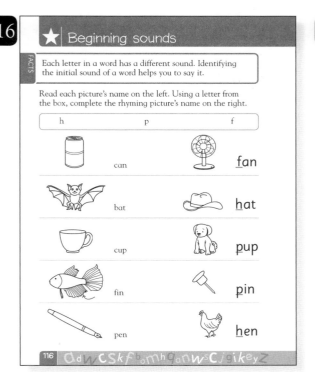

Each letter in a word has a different sound. Identifying the initial sound of a word helps you to say it.

Read each picture's name on the left. Using a letter from the box, complete the rhyming picture's name on the right.

| h | p | f |

can   <u>f</u>an

bat   <u>h</u>at

cup   <u>p</u>up

fin   <u>p</u>in

pen   <u>h</u>en

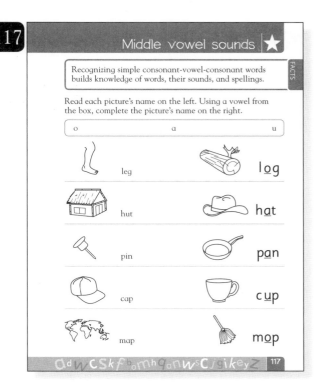

Recognizing simple consonant-vowel-consonant words builds knowledge of words, their sounds, and spellings.

Read each picture's name on the left. Using a vowel from the box, complete the picture's name on the right.

| o | a | u |

leg   l<u>o</u>g

hut   h<u>a</u>t

pin   p<u>a</u>n

cap   c<u>u</u>p

map   m<u>o</u>p

Write rhyming words on index cards, using specific-coloured markers for each group of words. For example, red for words ending in "-up," blue for words ending in "-at," and green for words ending in "-ad." Let your child identify the rhyme and sort the cards into groups.

Reinforce sounds and letters. Use a dark marker to write the five vowels at the bottom of five small paper cups. After working on the page, review the 10 words and ask your child to identify the paper cup with the correct vowel for each word.

★ Final sounds

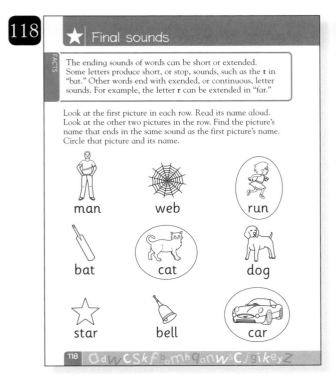

The ending sounds of words can be short or extended. Some letters produce short, or stop, sounds, such as the **t** in "bat." Other words end with exended, or continuous, letter sounds. For example, the letter **r** can be extended in "far."

Look at the first picture in each row. Read its name aloud. Look at the other two pictures in the row. Find the picture's name that ends in the same sound as the first picture's name. Circle that picture and its name.

man   web   run

bat   cat   dog

star   bell   car

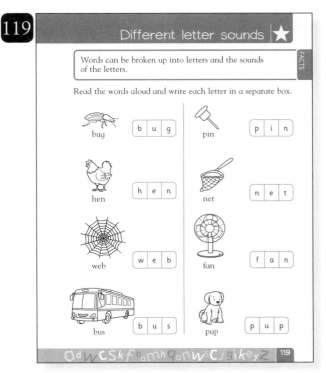

Words can be broken up into letters and the sounds of the letters.

Read the words aloud and write each letter in a separate box.

bug | b | u | g | pin | p | i | n |

hen | h | e | n | net | n | e | t |

web | w | e | b | fan | f | a | n |

bus | b | u | s | pup | p | u | p |

Read the words "sun" and "moon." Ask your child if they end with the same sound. Then say the words "door" and "book." Ask if they end with the same sound. Explore saying and writing words with the same ending sounds as "door." Examples are "floor," "car," and "your."

As an extension to this activity, find some more simple consonant-vowel-consonant words and practise breaking these words up into sounds with your child.

120

★ The long "a" sound

The long sound of the vowel **a** says its name. You hear the long "a" sound in the word "snake."

Read each picture's name aloud. Circle the names of the six pictures that have the long "a" sound. Make an **X** on the names of the two pictures that have the short "a" sound, as heard in "cat."

Read the sentence below. Circle the two words that have the long "a" sound.

Owen and I like to play in the rain.

Reinforce that long vowel sounds say the name of the vowel. Use a set of cards or magnetic letters and say each vowel. With your child, write a list of words with the long "a" sound.

121

The long "e" sound ★

The long sound of the vowel **e** says its name. You hear the long "e" sound in the word "cheese."

Read each picture's name aloud. Circle the names of the six pictures that have the long "e" sound. Make an **X** on the names of the two pictures that have the short "e" sound, as heard in "pen."

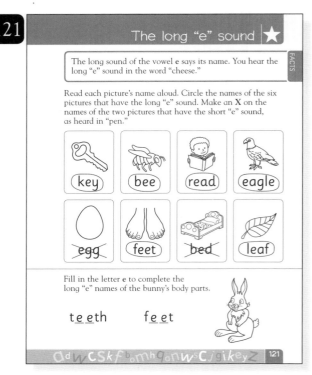

Fill in the letter **e** to complete the long "e" names of the bunny's body parts.

te_e_eth   fe_e_et

Help your child distinguish the long vowel sound of the letter **e** from the short "e" sound. Find pictures of things with both sounds. Engage him or her in sorting the pictures into two containers, one labeled "short vowel" and the other "long vowel."

★ The long "i" sound

The long sound of the vowel **i** says its name. You hear the long "i" sound in the word "lion."

Read each picture's name aloud. Circle the names of the six pictures that have the long "i" sound. Make an **X** on the names of the two pictures that have the short "i" sound, as heard in "tin."

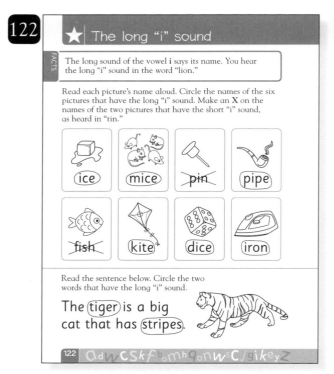

Read the sentence below. Circle the two words that have the long "i" sound.

The tiger is a big cat that has stripes.

Cut a large piece of construction paper into the shape of a kite and attach a tail with a piece of string. With your child, find and write the long "i" words on small cards. Tape the cards to the tail. Use these words to write a poem with your child.

The long "o" sound ★

The long sound of the vowel **o** says its name. You hear the long "o" sound in the word "boat."

Read each picture's name aloud. Circle the names of the six pictures that have the long "o" sound. Make an **X** on the names of the two pictures that have the short "o" sound, as heard in "pot."

Read the sentence below. Circle the two words that have the long "o" sound.

Jenny likes to eat yogourt and toast.

Draw an oval on a large sheet of paper. Write some long "o" and short "o" words on small cards. Guide your child to identify and then tape the cards with long "o" words onto the oval.

★ | The long "u" sound

FACTS

The long sound of the vowel **u** says its name. You hear the long "u" sound in the word "cube."

Read the words on the balloons aloud. Colour the five balloons that have words with the long "u" sound. Make an **X** on the two balloons that have words with the short "u" sound, as heard in "fun."

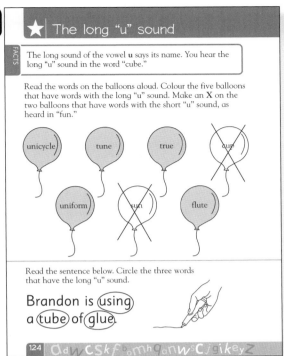

Read the sentence below. Circle the three words that have the long "u" sound.

Brandon is (using) a (tube) of (glue).

Review the long "u" sound by writing a short rhyme with your child. For example, "Does the boy in blue have the glue?" or "The unicorn wore a uniform."

The tricky letter y | ★

FACTS

The letter **y** can be tricky. Sometimes, it makes the long "e" vowel sound, as in the word "funny." Sometimes, it makes the long "i" vowel sound, as in the word "sky."

Circle the letter **y** in each word below. Read the word aloud. Listen to the "e" sound **y** makes in each word.

Write the letter **y** to complete each word below. Read the word aloud. Listen to the "i" sound **y** makes in each word.

Say words that end in the letter **y**, emphasizing the final sound, such as "carry," "silly," "sly," "spy," "lucky," "hungry," "why," and "dry." Ask your child to hold up a card showing the letter **e** or **i**, depending on the sound of **y** in each word.

★ | The short "a" sound

FACTS

The word "apple" begins with the short sound of the vowel **a**. Some other words with the short "a" sound are "cat," "bag," and "rat."

Circle the names of the four pictures that have the short "a" sound. Make an **X** on the names of the two pictures that have the long "a" sound.

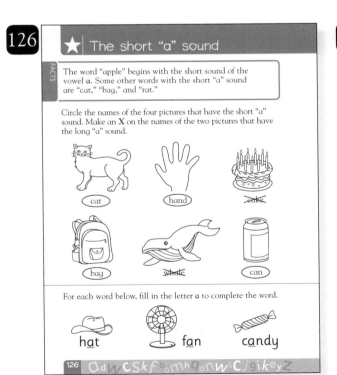

For each word below, fill in the letter **a** to complete the word.

h<u>a</u>t   f<u>a</u>n   c<u>a</u>ndy

Give your child a card with the letter **a**. Then give him or her a card with a consonant and ask your child to place the consonant before the **a**. Ask him or her to think of words that begin with those two letters. Finally, ask whether each word has a long or short "a" sound.

The short "e" sound | ★

FACTS

The word "egg" begins with the short sound of the vowel **e**. You also hear the short "e" sound in the words "jet," "desk," and "hen."

Read each picture's name in the word wheel aloud. Colour each section of the wheel in which the picture's name has the short "e" sound.

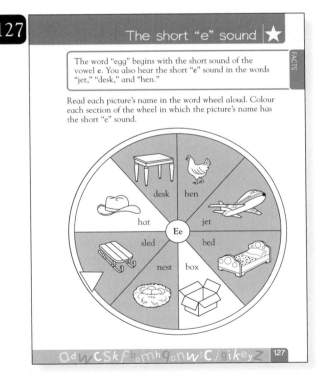

Reinforce the sounds of the letter **e**. List words with both long and short "e" sounds. Read them randomly. Let your child show an index card labelled "long" or "short" based on the letter sound he or she hears in each word. Examples include "pet," "bean," "met," "meet," "red," and "bead."

★ The short "i" sound

The word "pin" has the short sound of the vowel **i**. You also hear the short "i" sound in the words "pig," "fin," and "fish."

Read each picture's name in the word wheel aloud.
If the word has the short "i" sound, underline the letter **i**.
Make an **X** on the words that have the long "i" sound.

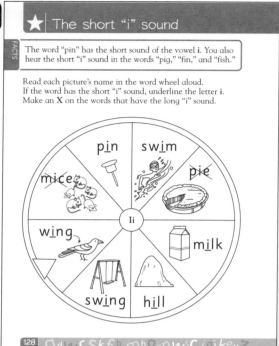

Help your child see words in context. Write sentences with short "i" words. Read them aloud, emphasizing the short "i" words. Then ask which words have the short "i" sound. An example of a sentence could be "The *little pig* had a curly tail."

The short "o" sound ★

The word "dog" has the short sound of the vowel **o**. You also hear the short "o" sound in the words "top" and "mop."

Read each picture's name aloud. Circle the six names that have the short "o" sound. Make an **X** on the two names that have the long "o" sound.

Read the sentence below. Circle the three words that have the short "o" sound.

The dog jumped over a log to run after the frog.

Record your voice reading words with the short "o" sound. Let your child read some words and record his or her voice. Listen to the recording as you view a list of words that includes those recorded. Help your child identify and highlight the words he or she hears.

★ The short "u" sound

The word "umbrella" has the short sound of the vowel **u**. You also hear the short "u" sound in the words "drum," "pup," and "sun."

Read each picture's name aloud. Circle the six names that have the short "u" sound. Make an **X** on the two names that have the long "u" sound.

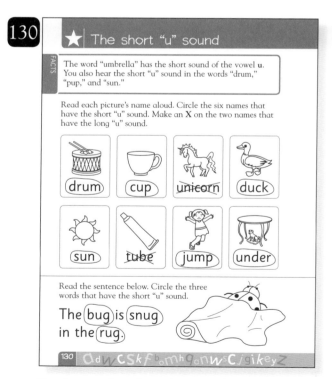

Read the sentence below. Circle the three words that have the short "u" sound.

The bug is snug in the rug.

Read pairs of words, such as "run fun," "pan can," and "bump jump." Some words should have the short sound of the letter **u**, and the others should not. Let your child show a thumbs-up for the pairs with the short "u" sound and a thumbs-down for the others.

Letters and words ★

The individual letter sounds in simple words can be changed to make new words.

Read each picture's name on the left. Fill in the letter to complete the picture's name on the right.

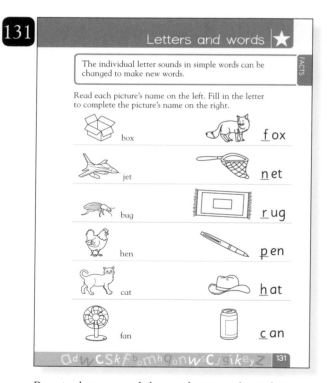

box   f ox

jet   n et

bug   r ug

hen   p en

cat   h at

fan   c an

Practise letter sounds by emphasizing those that your child may find challenging to hear and identify. Examples are "n" and "m," "b" and "p," and "d" and "t." Have your child show a letter card when he or she hears a particular sound.

★ Beginning sounds

To identify spoken words, let your child listen to the beginning sounds of the words.

Look at the picture of each animal. Say the letter on the animal aloud. Then draw a line to match each animal to its name.

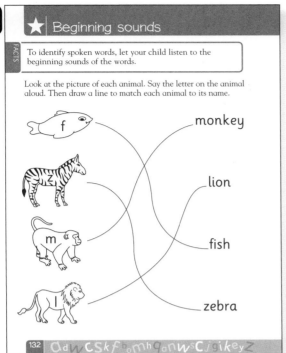

monkey

lion

fish

zebra

After your child works on this page, encourage him or her to think of more animal names. Ask your child to tell you the beginning letter of each name.

Rhyming words ★

Rhyming words have the same ending sound. For example, "cap" and "nap" end with the same letter sound.

Read the pictures' names in each box aloud. Circle "yes" if the words rhyme and "no" if the words do not rhyme.

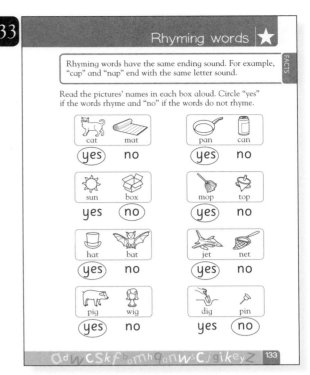

cat mat   (yes) no   pan can   (yes) no

sun box   yes (no)   mop top   (yes) no

hat bat   (yes) no   jet net   (yes) no

pig wig   (yes) no   dig pin   yes (no)

Read nursery rhymes aloud with your child. Emphasize the rhyming words. Let your child see the words and guide him or her to point to the words that rhyme.

★ Syllables

Every word has one or more syllables, or beats. For example, the word "boat" has one syllable, the word "butter" has two syllables, and the word "dinosaur" has three syllables.

Read each animal's name aloud. As you say the word, count the number of its syllables. Circle the correct number.

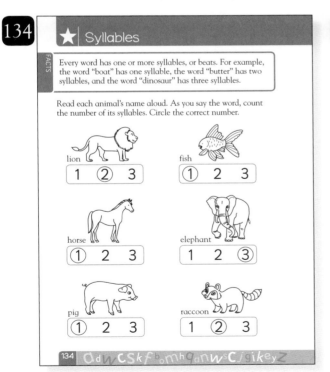

lion   1 (2) 3   fish   (1) 2 3

horse   (1) 2 3   elephant   1 2 (3)

pig   (1) 2 3   raccoon   1 (2) 3

While you are working through this page, clap your hands, or bang on a toy drum or a metal pot to emphasize the number of syllables in each word. After that, encourage your child to say names of family members and friends and count the number of syllables in each name.

More syllables ★

Every syllable has one vowel sound. For example, the word "tomato" has three vowel sounds and three syllables.

Read each sentence aloud. Circle the number of syllables in each underlined word.

My snack today is a banana.
1   2   (3)

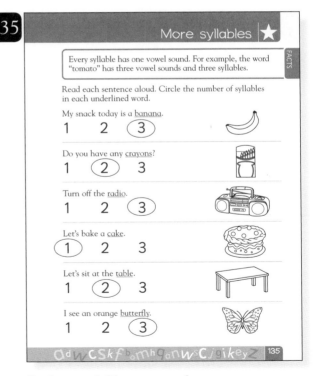

Do you have any crayons?
1   (2)   3

Turn off the radio.
1   2   (3)

Let's bake a cake.
(1)   2   3

Let's sit at the table.
1   (2)   3

I see an orange butterfly.
1   2   (3)

Guide your child to create a few sentences and help him or her write them down. In each sentence, examine the words and in each word, the syllables. Encourage him or her to count the syllables. Dinosaur names, such as "stegosaurus," can be particularly exciting examples.

136 ★ Sight words

FACTS

Sight words, or high-frequency words, are words commonly used in speaking and writing. The spelling of some of these words does not follow the usual letter-sound pattern.

Practise reading and using the sight words listed below.

all	four	on	too
am	get	please	under
are	good	ran	was
at	have	say	what
be	he	she	who
but	into	so	will
came	like	that	with
did	no	there	yes
do	now	they	you
eat	of	this	your

136 a d w c s k f b o m h g a n w s c j g i k e y z

Write these words on cards. With your child, practise using them to create sentences. The next time you are reading a story with your child, encourage him or her to identify sight words in the text.

137 Using sight words ★

FACTS

Learning to spell and use sight words improves fluency in reading.

Read each sentence below. Circle the correct sight word to complete the sentence.

I know the days (of) has the week.

Do (you) your have a red crayon?

Does (she) her have a brother?

That girl be (is) my friend.

Kate went (to) am the zoo.

A cat is in so (the) tree.

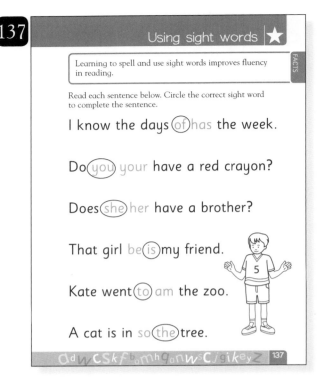

a d w c s k f b o m h g a n w s c j g i k e y z 137

Your child learns sight words, or high-frequency words, by repeatedly seeing and using them. Write sentences with the sight words missing. Let your child choose the word that makes the most sense.

138 ★ Letters make words

FACTS

Words are made with letters that are placed in order from left to right.

Find the words from the word box in the rectangles below. Each rectangle has three words hidden in it. Circle the words and read them aloud.

bat	cat	milk	rat	dog
drum	doll	plum	apple	

Food Words

(a p p l e) g o j (p l u m) q v (m i l k)

Toy Words

(d o l l) r j h i (b a t) x (d r u m) x

Animal Words

(c a t) j z p (r a t) g u l (d o g) s e

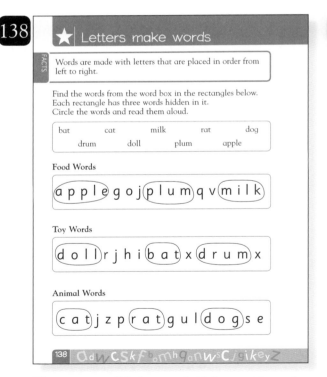

138 a d w c s k f b o m h g a n w s c j g i k e y z

This activity will help your child distinguish words from random groups of letters. By seeing groups of concept words, he or she will see that words convey ideas and meanings. Introduce your child to simple word searches that contain three-letter words.

139 Reading print ★

FACTS

Print, or written text, is made up of letters and words that are read from left to right.

Read the words in each sentence aloud. Circle the word at the end of each line.

I see a (bed).   I see a (tree).

I see a (horse).

I see a (jar).   I see a (kite).

a d w c s k f b o m h g a n w s c j g i k e y z 139

If necessary, help your child follow the pattern of reading word by word. Place a small card under each word as you read from left to right to reinforce the reading process.

★ Reading from left to right

Words in a sentence are read from left to right. At the end of a line, you return to the left side of the next line to continue reading.

Draw a line from the word in the box to the same word on the right.

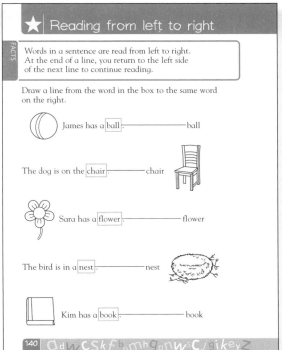

James has a ball ———— ball

The dog is on the chair ———— chair

Sara has a flower ———— flower

The bird is in a nest ———— nest

Kim has a book ———— book

While working through this page, reinforce the fact that each sentence conveys an idea or a thought. After reading, you could test your child on the spelling of some of the words on this page, such as "book," "nest," and "chair."

Reading and counting words ★

Words are combined to form sentences. The words in a sentence are separated by a single space between each word.

The sentences below tell a story. Count the words in each sentence. Circle the number of words each sentence contains.

I have a bear.

1   2   3   ④   5   6   7

It is a brown bear.

1   2   3   4   ⑤   6   7

It is not a big bear.

1   2   3   4   5   ⑥   7

The little bear sits in a chair.

1   2   3   4   5   6   ⑦

My little bear is a teddy bear.

1   2   3   4   5   6   ⑦

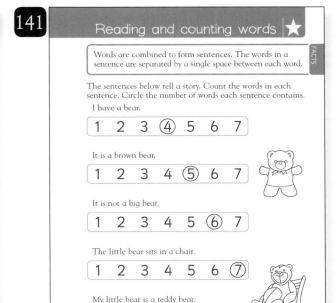

Help your child gain confidence as a reader as he or she counts the words in a sentence successfully. Point out the use of upper-case letters to begin sentences and punctuation, such as periods, to end sentences.

★ Words make sentences

Each sentence ends with a punctuation mark, such as a period (.).

Look at each sentence below. There is a space between each word in a sentence. Add a period at the end of each sentence. Read the sentence aloud.

I can jump.

I like swings.

My cat is asleep.

I can fly a kite.

Ask your child to look around him or her to think of some small sentences. Help your child to write them, and then draw attention to each word and its meaning. Encourage your child to use finger spaces between each word when writing.

Words make sentences ★

A sentence is a group of words that expresses a complete thought. Sentences can be long or short.

Read each sentence aloud. Count the words in each sentence and circle the correct number.

I like ice cream.

1   2   3   ④   5   6

I like vanilla ice cream.

1   2   3   4   ⑤   6

I like strawberry ice cream, too.

1   2   3   4   5   ⑥

I also like rainbow sprinkles.

1   2   3   4   ⑤   6

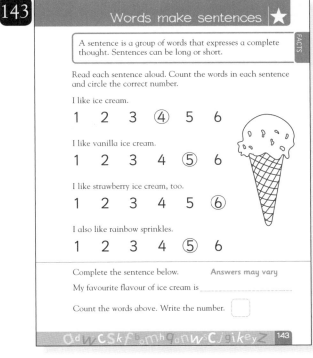

Complete the sentence below.   Answers may vary

My favourite flavour of ice cream is _____

Count the words above. Write the number. ☐

After completing this page, ask questions and guide your child to write simple sentences about one of his or her favourite things. Count the words in each sentence to show your child how he or she is forming ideas with words.

★ Rhyming sentences

FACTS Sentences that end with rhyming words are called rhyming sentences. Some poems have rhyming sentences.

Read each sentence aloud. Look at each picture and pick the correct word to complete the rhyme.

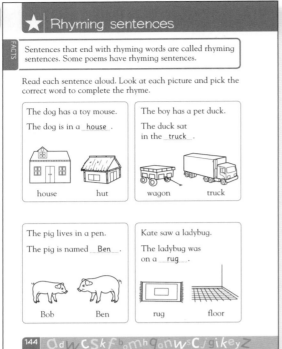

The dog has a toy mouse.
The dog is in a __house__.

house   hut

The boy has a pet duck.
The duck sat
in the __truck__.

wagon   truck

The pig lives in a pen.
The pig is named __Ben__.

Bob   Ben

Kate saw a ladybug.
The ladybug was
on a __rug__.

rug   floor

Your child will gain confidence as a reader as he or she reads each rhyme. Follow up this activity by reading simple poems from a book or from a website. Leave out some of the rhyming words and let your child fill them in.

Reading a story ★

FACTS You read words from left to right, top to bottom, and then page by page.

The pictures in the boxes below tell a story. Follow the numbers to read the story and answer the questions.

1 The puppy barks.
2 The puppy is given food.
3 The puppy eats her food.
4 Finally, the puppy sleeps.

In which picture does the puppy bark?   1

In which picture does the puppy eat?   3

In which picture does the puppy sleep?   4

In which picture is the puppy given food?   2

To check comprehension of the picture story on this page, ask questions such as "Why does the puppy bark?" Point out the numbers on each picture and reinforce that there is a sequence of events in the story.

★ Reading a story

FACTS Knowing the sounds that letters make helps children recognize words and builds reading skills.

Read the story aloud. Circle the correct word to answer each question.

A Puppy Named Pooky

Joey has a little puppy.
She is a funny puppy.
The puppy is named Pooky.
One day, Pooky went to hide.
Where are you, Pooky?
Pooky was under the table.

What is the story about?

a cat   (a puppy)

Is the puppy big or little?

big   (little)

What is the name of the puppy?

Joey   (Pooky)

Where was Pooky hiding?

(under the table)   under the bed

Reading words and listening to their sounds carefully is a step toward comprehending text. As your child listens to a story, he or she begins to see that words have meaning. Check his or her understanding of text. Read the text slowly, then repeat it. Review it before asking questions.

Reading to understand ★

FACTS Children should be able to read with purpose and understanding. Regular reading reinforces fluency so that children read accurately, quickly, and with expression.

Read all about the life of a frog in the four boxes. Pick the correct word to complete each sentence below.

The Life of a Frog

1. "Ribbit!" That may be a frog calling. Let's visit the pond. Frogs live on land and in water.

2. Many frogs eat insects. They use their long tongues to catch them.

3. Frogs have long, strong back legs. They are good jumpers and swimmers.

4. Frogs lay eggs. The eggs hatch into tadpoles. The tadpoles grow up to be frogs.

Frogs live on land and in __water__.   water   caves

Many frogs eat __insects__.   insects   fish

Frogs have long back __legs__.   tails   legs

Frogs are good __jumpers__.   jumpers   crawlers

Let your child listen to the real-life information on this page one or two times before he or she answers the questions. If your child does not recall the information, show him or her how to look back at the text to find answers.

⭐ The lower-case alphabet

FACTS

Lower-case letters are the small letters.
The first letters of the alphabet are **a** through **n**.

Trace lower-case letters **a** through **n**.
Then write these letters in lower case on your own.

a a a a a a a art	h h h h h h h ham
b b b b b b b bad	i i i i i i i ill
c c c c c c c cat	j j j j j j j jet
d d d d d d d dot	k k k k k k k kit
e e e e e e e egg	l l l l l l l lot
f f f f f f f fit	m m m m m mad
g g g g g g g get	n n n n n n n not

Children can also practise writing other simple
three-letter words in lower-case letters. Help them
think of words that begin with **a** through **n**.

The lower-case alphabet ⭐

FACTS

The letters in most words are in lower case.
The last letters of the alphabet are **o** through **z**.

Trace lower-case letters **o** through **z**.
Then write these letters in lower case on your own.

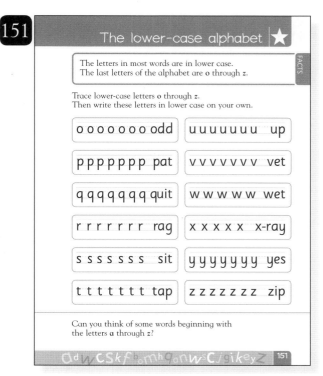

o o o o o o o odd	u u u u u u u up
p p p p p p p pat	v v v v v v v vet
q q q q q q q quit	w w w w w w wet
r r r r r r r rag	x x x x x x-ray
s s s s s s s sit	y y y y y y y yes
t t t t t t t tap	z z z z z z z zip

Can you think of some words beginning with
the letters *a* through *z*?

Have your child look in books for short, simple
words starting with **o** through **z** and set in lower
case. Children can copy the words and name
the letters as they write. Read the words with
your child.

⭐ The upper-case alphabet

FACTS

Upper-case letters are used in the names of people, places,
or events. These are the letters **A** through **N** in upper case.

Practise writing the upper-case letters. First trace the letters.
Then write upper-case letters **A** through **N** on your own.

A A A A A April	H H H H Hannah
B B B B B Brad	I I I I I I I Ivan
C C C C C C Cody	J J J J J J Joe
D D D D D D Dan	K K K K K K Kim
E E E E E Emma	L L L L L Logan
F F F F F F Fred	M M M Morgan
G G G G Grace	N N N N N Nora

Invite children to write their first and last names
with correct capitalization.

The upper-case alphabet ⭐

FACTS

Upper-case letters are used at the beginning of a sentence
and in titles. Here are the letters **O** through **Z** in upper case.

Practise writing the upper-case letters. First trace the letters.
Then write upper-case letters **O** through **Z** on your own.

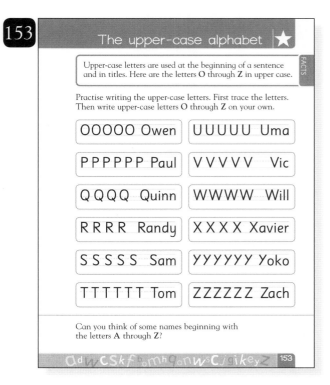

O O O O O Owen	U U U U U Uma
P P P P P P Paul	V V V V V Vic
Q Q Q Q Quinn	W W W W Will
R R R R Randy	X X X X Xavier
S S S S S Sam	Y Y Y Y Y Yoko
T T T T T Tom	Z Z Z Z Z Z Zach

Can you think of some names beginning with
the letters **A** through **Z**?

Continue to practise upper-case writing by writing
the name of your street and city.

★ Book time

FACTS

Books have covers. Covers give information about books.

Description	Instruction
The title is the name of the book.	Look at the book's cover. Draw a box around the title.
The author is the person who wrote the book.	Draw a line under the author's name.
A book title uses upper-case letters. People's names also start with upper-case letters.	Circle all the upper-case letters.
The title and picture on a book's cover can give you a clue as to what the book will be about.	What do you think you would read in this book? Finally, colour the book cover.

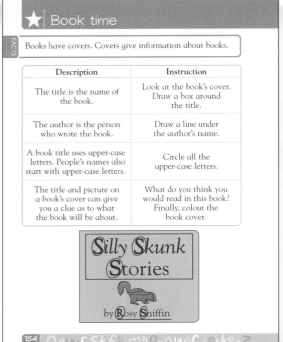

Silly Skunk Stories
by Rosy Shiffin

When you read books with your children, point out the features on the cover: title, author, and illustrator. Invite children to make predictions about the story based on the information on the cover. If the book is a familiar one, talk about why the cover illustration is (or is not) a good choice for the book.

Tell a story ★

FACTS

Stories have a beginning, a middle, and an end.

Look at the pictures below. Then tell the story they show aloud. What happens first? What happens next? What happens last? When you have told the story, colour the pictures.
Answers may vary

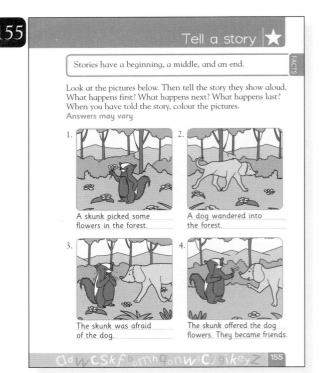

1. A skunk picked some flowers in the forest.
2. A dog wandered into the forest.
3. The skunk was afraid of the dog.
4. The skunk offered the dog flowers. They became friends.

After reading books to children, invite them to retell what happens first, next, and at the end. Help your child write a sentence about each drawing. Read it back together.

★ Short "a"

FACTS

The letter **a** can sound like the **a** in "apple" (short "a") or the **a** in "ape" (long "a").

Each word is missing its short "a." Write the letter to complete the word. Then read each word aloud.

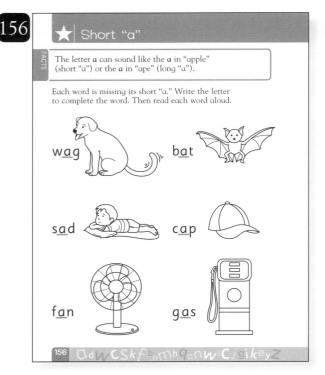

wag   bat

sad   cap

fan   gas

Find simple words in books that have an **a**, and ask your child if the **a** is short or long. The short and long vowel sounds are introduced with your support. Your child will become more familiar with them in Grades 1 and 2.

Rhyming words ★

FACTS

Two words that end in the same sound are called rhyming words. Rhyming words begin with different sounds.

Read the sentences aloud. Draw a line under the rhyming words.

My <u>dad</u> was <u>mad</u>.

A <u>mat</u> is <u>flat</u>.

Put the <u>rag</u> in the <u>bag</u>.

The <u>rat</u> <u>sat</u> on the cap.

Encourage your child to think of other short "a" rhymes. Offer help in writing them down.

★ Rhyming match

Rhyming words often have similar spellings. Sometimes rhyming words can have completely different spellings.

Read each word aloud. Find the pairs of rhyming words in the balloons. Colour each pair the same colour.

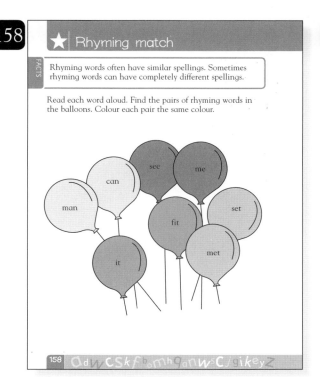

Invite your child to name other words that rhyme with the words in the balloons. Write them on the page.

Nursery rhymes ★

A nursery rhyme is a poem or song for children. Nursery rhymes are passed down through the years.

Read the nursery rhyme aloud. Underline the rhyming words. Draw a picture that illustrates the nursery rhyme.

Hey, <u>diddle</u>, <u>diddle</u>,
The cat and the <u>fiddle</u>,
The cow jumped over the <u>moon</u>.
The little dog laughed
To see such sport,
And the dish ran away with the <u>spoon</u>.
Drawings may vary

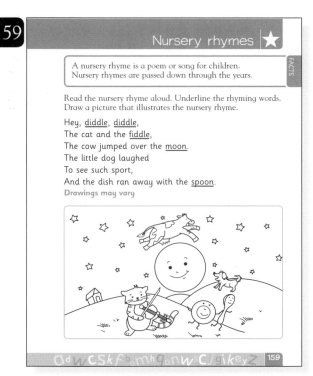

What other nursery rhymes do you know? Repeat this activity with other favourites.

★ Spot the rhymes

Saying words aloud can make it easier to figure out if they rhyme. Here are some more rhyming words to practise.

Find the rhyming words. Draw a line between each pair.

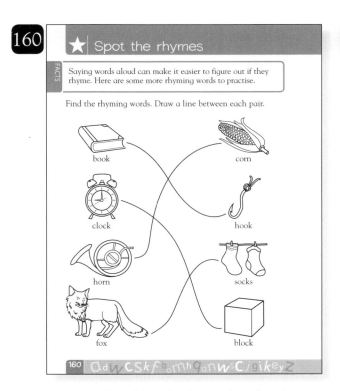

Point out that although "fox" and "socks" rhyme, they do not end with the same letters.

Complete the sentences ★

Some words are used often in reading and writing. You can learn to recognize these words.

Read the words aloud. Use them to complete sentences.

off	out	from	in	to	for

I gave the bag ___to___ Bob.

The gift is ___for___ you.

Jane took the book ___from___ me.

The dog is ___in___ the house.

We are ___out___ of the car.

The lid is ___off___ the pot.

The most often used words by children per grade level for reading and writing are called "sight words." Look online for sight word lists for your child's grade level, which will help you understand which words your child should recognize instantly.

⭐ Story characters

FACTS A character is a person or animal in a story.

Read the story aloud.

A wolf liked to look at the stars. One night,
he walked along looking up at the stars.
He didn't see a hole in the ground and fell into it.
Another wolf passing by said, "You see the stars far
away. Why don't you see the ground under your feet?"

Below, circle the character that this story is about.

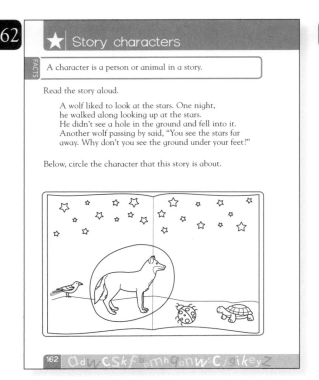

Invite your child to name and describe favourite
characters from well-known stories.

Story setting ⭐

FACTS A setting is where and when a story takes place.

Read the story aloud.

Jenny and Jack climbed on a sled. They zoomed
down a hill. The winter air turned their cheeks cold.
The sled stopped at the bottom of the hill.
Jack said, "Let's ride again!"

Circle the picture that shows the setting of the story.

As you read books to your child, point out details
about the setting. Talk about how the setting
adds to the story.

⭐ Short "e"

FACTS The letter e can sound like the e in "egg"
(short "e") or the e in "eel" (long "e").

Each word is missing its short "e." Write the letter
to complete the word. Then read each word aloud.

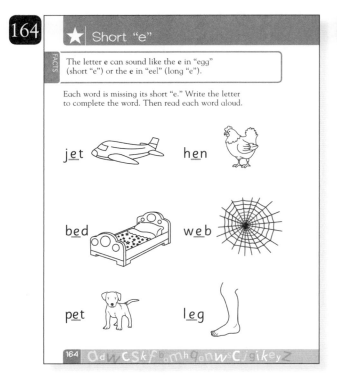

jet   hen

bed   web

pet   leg

Find simple words in books that have an e.
Read them with your child and ask if the word
has a short "e" or a long "e."

Rhyming words ⭐

FACTS Rhyming words in a sentence make it more fun
to read. Here are some more rhyming words.

Read the sentences aloud. Draw lines under
the rhyming words.

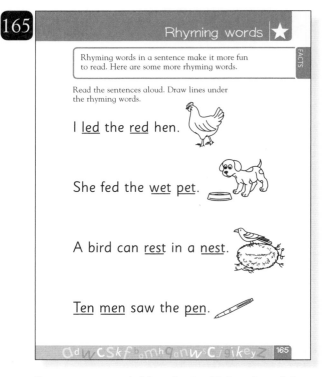

I led the red hen.

She fed the wet pet.

A bird can rest in a nest.

Ten men saw the pen.

Encourage your child to think of other short "e"
rhymes. Help your child write them.

★ Information

FACTS

People read for different reasons.
Sometimes they read to learn.

Read the text below.

A map helps you find your way. A map can show your home. It can show your school. A map can show you how to go from your home to your school.

Circle the picture that shows what the text is about.

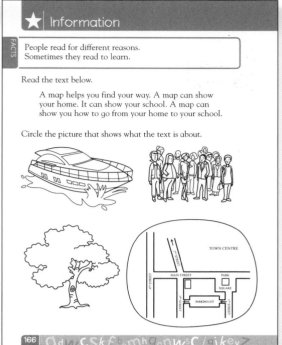

Describe examples of things you read to learn: for example, newspapers, books, cookbooks, and instructions.

Labels ★

FACTS

Labels are a text feature.
They give information about a picture.

Write labels naming the parts of the tiger.
Use the words from the word bank.

| back | ear | eye | leg | nose | tail |

ear

eye

back

nose

tail

leg

Look for examples of labels in texts around your home. Point them out to your child.

★ Spot the person, place, or thing

FACTS

Some words name a person, a place, or a thing.

Circle the words that name a person, a place, or a thing.

bird

run

train

man

pull

leaf

car

book

Your child may not be familiar with the term "noun" until the next grade. Introduce the term if you think your child will understand. Ask your child to name other people, places, or things around the house.

Spot the action word ★

FACTS

An action word names anything one can do or be.

Circle the action words.

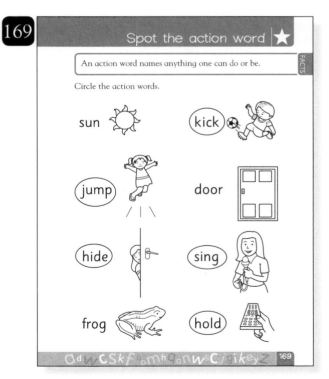

sun

kick

jump

door

hide

sing

frog

hold

Your child may not be familiar with the term "verb." Invite your child to name other action words and act them out: for example, "dance," "skip," and "wiggle."

⭐ Short "i"

FACTS The letter **i** can sound like the **i** in "big" (short "i") or the **i** in "ripe" (long "i").

Each word is missing its short "i." Write the letter to complete the word. Then read each word aloud.

d_i_g   k_i_d

s_i_t   r_i_p

b_i_b   p_i_n

Find simple words in books that have an i. Read them with your child and ask your child if the word has a short "i" or long "i."

Rhyming words ⭐

FACTS One way to create a word that rhymes with another word is to change the first letter of the word.

Make rhyming words using letters from the letter bank.

Answers may vary

r	d	w	p	f	t

_t_in   _f_in

_d_id   _r_id

_p_ig   _w_ig

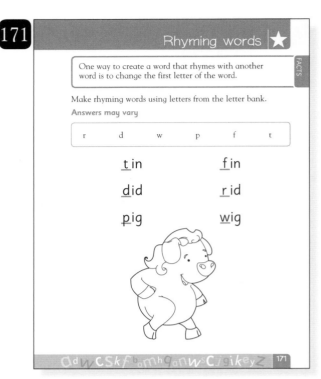

Encourage your child to think of other short "i" rhyming words. Offer help when writing the words.

⭐ Describe the word

FACTS Some words describe people, places, or things.

Draw a line between the picture and the word that describes it.

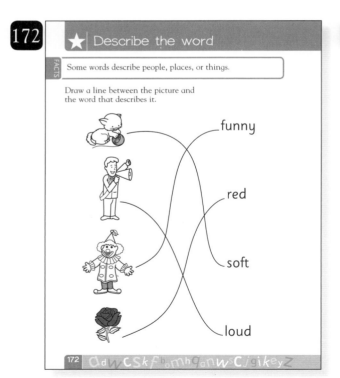

funny

red

soft

loud

Your chid may not be familiar with the term "adjective." Introduce the term if you think your child will understand. Ask your child to describe objects you see around you.

First, next, last ⭐

FACTS Telling or writing information in order helps it make sense.

This story is out of order. What happens first, next, and last? Write 1, 2, and 3 by the pictures to put them in the correct order.

Ask your child to retell other stories using words such as "first," "second," "next," "then," "finally," and "last." These words convey time and order.

★ Ordering events

FACTS Make sense of information by telling or writing it in order.

Read the text below. Then look at the pictures. Number the pictures 1, 2, 3, and 4 to show the order in which the story happened.

Meg wanted to sell lemonade. First, she made the lemonade. Next, she set up her stand. Then, she hung up a sign. Finally, Meg sold lots of lemonade to her friends!

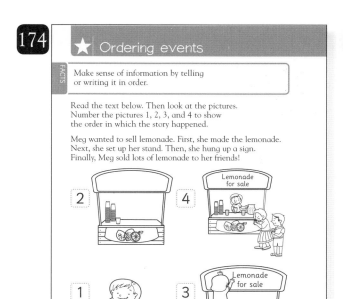

Have your child retell the story in order using words such as "first," "second," "next," "then," "finally," and "last."

Short "o" ★

FACTS The letter **o** can sound like the **o** in "dog" (short "o") or the **o** in "rope" (long "o").

Each word is missing its short "o." Write the letter to complete the word. Then read each word aloud.

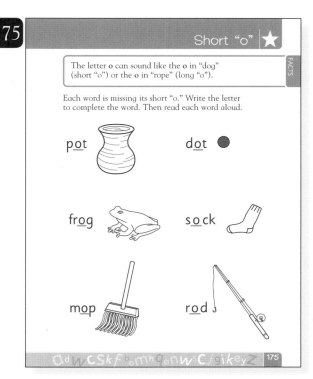

p_o_t   d_o_t

frog   s_o_ck

mop   r_o_d

Find simple words in books that have an **o**. Read them with your child and ask your child if the word has a short "o" or long "o."

★ Rhyming words

FACTS If words end with the same sound, they are rhyming words.

Read the sentences aloud. Circle the rhyming words.

The (cat) sits on the (mat).

(Bob) likes corn on the (cob).

Lots of (dogs) sit on (logs).

The (pot) is (not) too (hot).

While you read the sentences aloud, invite your child to point to other words that have a short "o" sound, even if they don't rhyme. For instance, "on," "lots," and "of."

Sorting ★

FACTS Words can name a general idea or topic, such as "place" or "job." Other words are more specific, such as "city" or "teacher."

Find the words that name foods in the spaces. Colour those spaces red. Find the words that name animals in the spaces. Colour those spaces green.

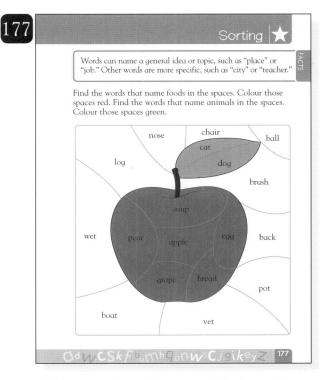

Collect some objects from around the house that have a similar theme: for example, toys and tools. Have your child sort and group the items and name the word that describes each group.

★ Plurals add **s**

FACTS

Singular means one. Plural means more than one. To make some words plural, add an **s** at the end of the word.

Make these words plural.

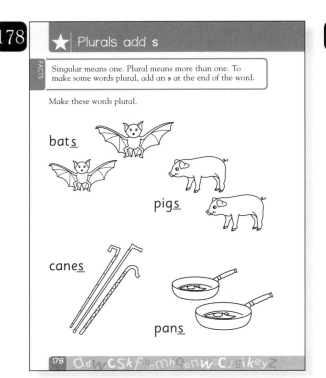

bat**s**

pig**s**

cane**s**

pan**s**

Look for singular and plural words in storybooks, and ask your child which ones mean "one" and which ones are "more than one."

More plurals with **s** ★

FACTS

To make some words plural, add an **s** at the end of the word.

Make these words plural.

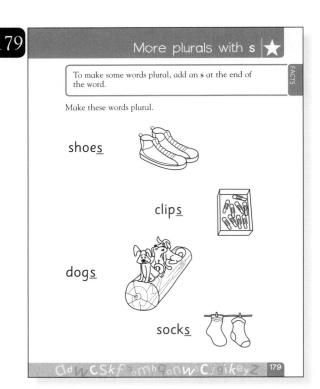

shoe**s**

clip**s**

dog**s**

sock**s**

Brainstorm other words that can be made more than one with an **s**. Your child will become more familiar with plurals in the next grade.

★ My favourite storybook

FACTS

A story has a title, or name. Stories are made up by authors. Stories also have characters and a setting.

Find one of your favourite storybooks to read together. Write down the title, author, characters, and setting of the story. Write down why you like it.

My favourite storybook

Title: **Answers may vary**

Author: **Answers may vary**

Characters: **Answers may vary**

Setting: **Answers may vary**

Why I like this book: **Answers may vary**

Draw a picture of something that happens in your favourite storybook.

Answers may vary

Have your child find a favourite storybook to complete this activity. Take time to read the storybook together. Write the answers to this activity together.

My favourite true book ★

FACTS

Some books are about true events. Some books inform us about a subject.

Find a favourite book that is about true events to read together. Write down the title, author, and subject of the book. Write down why you like it.

My favourite true book

Title: **Answers may vary**

Author: **Answers may vary**

Subject: **Answers may vary**

Why I like this book: **Answers may vary**

Draw a picture of what your favourite true book is about.

Answers may vary

You child will not be familiar with the term "non-fiction" at this stage, so help him or her to understand the concept. Help your child find a favourite non-fiction book to read and write about together.

★ Short "u"

FACTS
The letter **u** can sound like the **u** in "up" (short "u") or the **u** in "use" (long "u").

Each word is missing its short "u." Write the letter to complete the word. Then read each word aloud.

r_u_g

bud

hut

cub

bus

pup

Find simple words in books that have a **u**. Read them with your child and ask your child if the word has a short "u" or long "u."

Rhyming words ★

FACTS
Using a rhyme in a sentence can make it easier to remember.

Read the sentences aloud. Draw lines under the rhyming words.

It is <u>fun</u> to <u>run</u>.

Can you <u>cut</u> a <u>nut</u>?

A <u>bug</u> is on the <u>mug</u>.

The <u>fox</u> is in the <u>box</u>.

Encourage your child to think of other short "u" rhymes. Offer help in writing them. Also encourage your child to point out other short vowel sounds, such as the short "a" in "can" or the short "o" in "on."

★ Sound-alike words

FACTS
Some words sound alike but are spelled differently.

Read each pair of words aloud. They sound alike! Trace the letters that change the spelling of the words.

tea   tee

son   sun

toe   tow

tail   tale

hair   hare

blew   blue

Words that sound alike are called homophones, but your child will not be familiar with this term. They will become more familiar with sound-alike words in a later grade. What other sound-alike words can your child think of?

Action song ★

FACTS
This popular song names different parts of the body.

Sing or say the song. As you sing, point to the parts named. Then use words from the song to label the parts of the body.

Head, shoulders, knees and toes, knees and toes.
Head, shoulders, knees and toes, knees and toes.
And eyes, and ears and mouth and nose.
Head, shoulders, knees, and toes, knees and toes.

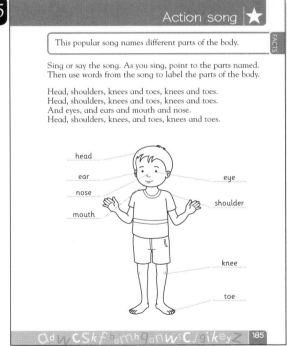

head
ear
nose
mouth
eye
shoulder
knee
toe

If you can, teach your child the movements that go with this song. This will make the song easier to remember.

★ Question words

FACTS

Question words help people think about and understand what they read, do, or see.

The animals are running a race in the park. Look at the picture. Then answer the questions.

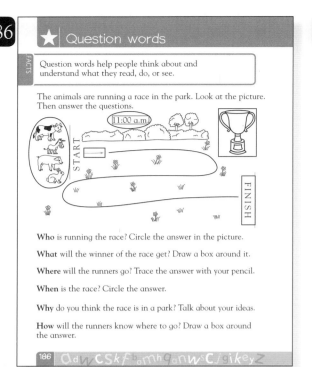

Who is running the race? Circle the answer in the picture.

What will the winner of the race get? Draw a box around it.

Where will the runners go? Trace the answer with your pencil.

When is the race? Circle the answer.

Why do you think the race is in a park? Talk about your ideas.

How will the runners know where to go? Draw a box around the answer.

Study the drawing with your child and read and answer the questions together. Here, children are invited to explain why they think the race is in a park. Answers will vary; there are no wrong answers. This is a good opportunity for children to think critically. For example, is running in a park safer than running in the streets?

Question words ★

FACTS

Question words are words that help people ask for information.

Select question words from the word bank to best complete each question. **Answers may vary**

| who | what | where | when | why | how |

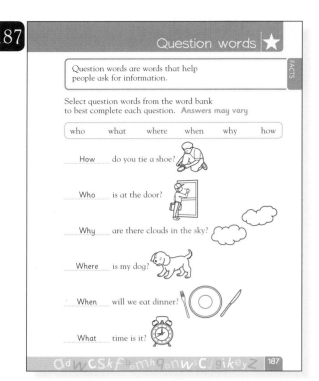

How do you tie a shoe?

Who is at the door?

Why are there clouds in the sky?

Where is my dog?

When will we eat dinner?

What time is it?

Be sure to encourage your child to write the letters with correct capitalization. Words that begin a sentence start with an upper-case letter. Encourage your child to ask questions using the question words. They will also learn and use these question words more in Grade 1.

★ Letters together

FACTS

Letters are used together to make new sounds.

Trace the letters to complete each word. Say the words aloud.

block

glue

clips

grapes

brush

crab

Letters that are not vowels are called consonants. Consonant letters that are used together to make new sounds are called blends. Children learn just basic words with one syllable at this level. Your child will learn more about blends in the next grade. Encourage your child to think of other words with the **bl, br, cl, cr, gl**, and **gr** consonant blends.

Sounds together ★

FACTS

Certain letters make special sounds when they are used together.

c + h makes the sound that starts the word "chip."
s + h makes the sound that starts the word "sheep."
t + h makes the sound that starts the word "thin."
Draw a line to connect each word to its sound.

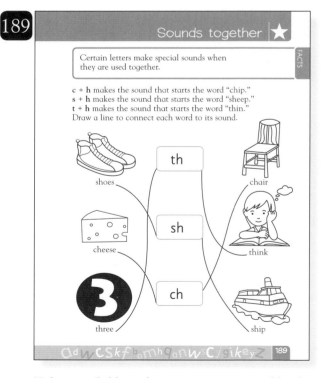

shoes

th

chair

cheese

sh

think

3

ch

three

ship

Help your child see that certain consonant blends used together make special sounds. Look together for signs that have the **ch**, **sh**, and **th** consonant blends. Point them out as you see them and read them aloud.

★ More than one meaning

Sometimes one word has more than one meaning.

Use the words in the word bank to write the names of the pictures. The first one has been done for you.

box	duck	fall	train

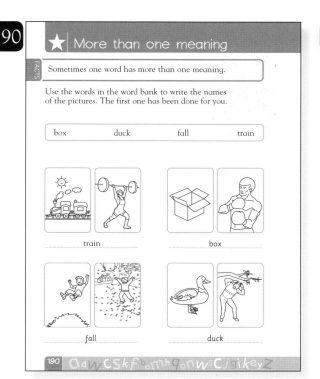

train

box

fall

duck

As you read or converse with your children, keep eyes and ears open for other words that have the same spelling but have two different meanings (for example, "walk," "shower," and hook.") In later grades your child will see how they work as nouns and verbs.

Writing letters ★

Every letter has an upper-case and a lower-case form.

For each letter, fill in the missing upper-case or lower-case letter.

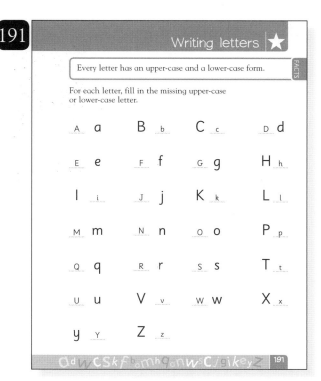

A a   B b   C c   D d

E e   F f   G g   H h

I i   J j   K k   L l

M m   N n   O o   P p

Q q   R r   S s   T t

U u   V v   W w   X x

y Y   Z z

For extra practice, have children write their names and complete address.

★ Writing words

Some words are easy to recognize. Others need to be sounded out.

Say the words describing these pictures aloud. Then write the words.

cat   fan   bed

nut   sit   pig

rug   cut   bat

For extra practice, invite children to write a note to a family member or have them help write a grocery list.

Write about it ★

People can share ideas and give information through writing.

Complete the sentences to describe your day.

My day

My name is Answers may vary   .

Here is what happened to me today/yesterday. (Circle one.)

First, Answers may vary

                                                      .

Then, Answers may vary

                                                      .

Finally, Answers may vary

                                                      .

I felt Answers may vary

                                                      !

This activity can be repeated regularly on separate pieces of paper. Tell your child that writing daily about one's thoughts and experiences is called keeping a journal. At this age, children may not want to take on a daily journal, but using this activity as a template for regular practice can build writing skills.